The Clinician's Guide to Exposure Therapies *for* Anxiety Spectrum Disorders

Integrating Techniques and Applications from CBT, DBT, and ACT

Timothy A. Sisemore, PhD

New Harbinger Publications, Inc.

Distributed in Canada by Raincoast Books

New Harbinger Publications, Inc.
5674 Shattuck Avenue
Oakland, CA 94609
www.newharbinger.com

Acquired by Tesilya Hanauer; Cover design by Amy Shoup;
Edited by Clancy Drake; Text design by Tracy Marie Carlson

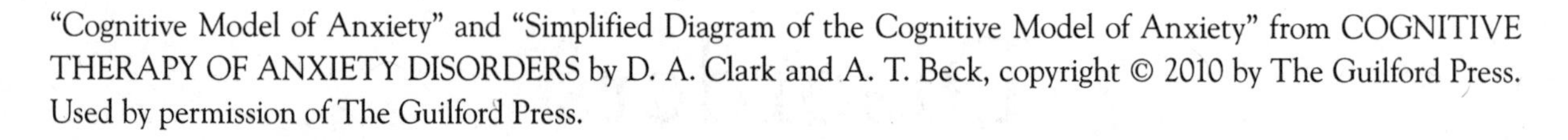

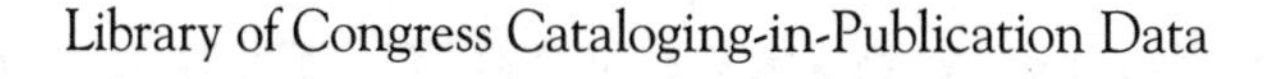

Library of Congress Cataloging-in-Publication Data

Sisemore, Timothy A.
The clinician's guide to exposure therapies for anxiety spectrum disorders : integrating techniques and applications from CBT, DBT, and ACT / Timothy A. Sisemore.
p. cm.
Summary: "The Clinician's Guide to Exposure Therapies for Anxiety Spectrum Disorders is a much-needed, organized manual that offers therapists a detailed menu of exposure exercises for the treatment of the most common fears and phobias. It includes strategies for increasing clients' willingness to participate in exposure therapy and incorporates the most effective therapy exercises from cognitive behavioral therapy, acceptance and commitment therapy, dialectical behavior therapy, and other modalities. Therapists can simply look up clients' symptoms to find the most effective exposure therapy treatment exercises for a client's particular anxiety issue"-- Provided by publisher.
Includes bibliographical references and index.
ISBN 978-1-60882-152-5 (pbk.) -- ISBN 978-1-60882-153-2 (pdf e-book) -- ISBN 978-1-60882-154-9 (epub) 1. Anxiety disorders--Treatment. 2. Exposure therapy. I. Title.
RC531.S57 2012
616.85'22--dc23

2012026564

Printed in the United States of America

14 13 12 10 9 8 7 6 5 4 3 2 1 First printing

Courage is being scared to death—but saddling up anyway.

—John Wayne

Contents

Part II

A Menu of Specific Suggestions for Exposure and Response Prevention

With Appreciation

When I began this project two years ago, I was under no illusions that I would be able to do this alone. I have been blessed to have a great supporting cast and wish to express my gratitude. Ron Bunger, librarian at Richmont Graduate University, has been gracious and diligent to round up a wealth of resources to support this book. Erin Rayburn, Jane Brandon, and Camilla Brown are students who have also contributed valuable time to helping with the literature review. The entire crew at New Harbinger has again proven helpful and encouraging, broadening and clarifying the vision for the project. Hats off also to Clancy Drake, whose careful editing made this much more readable than it might have been.

Most of all, I am grateful to and for my wife, Ruth, and daughter, Erin, who patiently cheered this project on—even though it took so much of my time.

Whatever good can be said of this book, I owe to this stellar group of supporters. The weaknesses that remain reveal my humanness that still shows despite such superb guidance and support.

—Timothy A. Sisemore, PhD
Chattanooga, TN
June 2012

Introduction

Exposure Therapy: A Tool for the Times

The environment for practicing psychotherapy is changing. Gone are the early days of my career, when I set a fee and insurance paid 80 percent of whatever (reasonable) amount I set. Even better, no care manager was looking over my shoulder to see how many sessions I took or what I was doing in them, leaving me free to practice as I thought best. I feel old just writing that, knowing that younger clinicians can hardly imagine such a world. While the freedom was delightful, I admit that it made it quite easy to do whatever you wished in therapy and be in no hurry about it. Exploitation was rampant, which was an expense to the payers and a disservice to clients. While I miss the unhurried pace, I greatly appreciate that there is more accountability for therapists to use the best methods in treating clients.

Yet the new dispensation has its downsides, including that, while managed care pushes therapists to use techniques supported by science, the best methods are not always the easiest or the most familiar. Exposure therapy (ET), and its companion, response prevention (RP), are excellent examples of unfamiliar but effective methods. Though they are undoubtedly evidence-based and typically relatively short-term, they are often overlooked by clinicians. That is of concern, as they effectively treat the spectrum of anxiety disorders, the most common group of mental health problems (Kessler, Chiu, Demler, & Walters, 2005).

The National Institute of Mental Health's (2009) brochure on anxiety disorders and their treatment lists only two recommended therapies: pharmacotherapy and cognitive behavioral therapy (CBT). However, much of the article focuses on the oft-forgotten "behavioral" part of CBT, which in this case is exposure therapy. Exposure therapy is mentioned specifically as a vital element of CBT in Antony's (2011) excellent summary of current treatments for anxiety. Despite such support, ET remains undervalued and relatively unknown. Yet, the bottom line is that it works. Forsyth, Barrios, and Acheson (2007, p. 70) state, "Numerous studies have shown that exposure therapy is efficacious in the treatment of all anxiety disorders." While these authors concede that ET does not help everyone, they confirm that 70 to 90 percent of those receiving ET benefit from it. It is time for ET to be used as frequently as the literature suggests it should.

This book is intended to help you better understand both exposure therapy and response prevention and to use them effectively. It provides a grounding in exposure therapies and response prevention and a guide to how to use them across the spectrum of anxiety disorders. Moreover, I will stress how exposure therapy and response prevention fit into the context of cognitive behavioral therapy and newer, "third-wave" versions of CBT. Dialectical behavior therapy (DBT) and acceptance and commitment therapy (ACT) are proving their mettle in research, and, as we'll see, exposure therapy serves a vital role in these.

Part I begins with an examination of the roots and development of exposure therapy and response prevention, and, in Chapter 2, a consideration of the evidence for these tools' effectiveness. In Chapter 3, we will see how escape and avoidance behaviors perpetuate anxiety and how these behaviors are to be addressed with ET and (particularly) RP. This sets the stage for a detailed exposition in Chapter 4 of how EP works and how it is to be implemented in counseling, including a discussion of the various types of exposures that may be used. The next chapters (5, 6, and 7) provide a discussion of how ET and RP fit in broader treatment plans based in cognitive behavioral therapy, dialectical behavior therapy, and acceptance and commitment therapy. Edna Foa (Foa, Hembree, & Rothbaum, 2007) has developed an important variant of ET called prolonged exposure therapy. An overview of this variation and its take on the role of emotional processing, along with accounts of narrative exposure therapy and emotion exposure, comprise Chapter 8. Chapter 9 is a guide to how to use the disorder-specific menus of exposure ideas in Part II.

Part II follows the proposed categories of the DSM-5 (drawn from the DSM development site: American Psychiatric Association, 2012) to list many of the most common fears to which ET can be applied, offering suggestions of *imaginal* (in one's imagination), *virtual reality, interoceptive* (physiological sensations associated with anxiety), and *in vivo* (in the actual situation) exposures to each as applicable. This is intended to stimulate your thinking and aid in customizing the principles of ET to individual client needs.

I hope that this book will give you effective, evidence-based tools to utilize in treating clients with anxiety, in conjunction with warm clinical regard for the client and understanding of the challenges anxiety poses. With gentle support, these tools can help many to live more meaningful and placid lives not controlled or burdened by undue anxiety.

PART I

The Many Facets of Exposure and Response Prevention

CHAPTER 1

Exposure Therapy: The Overlooked Treasure

Melanie has had enough. She has worked hard to overcome her fears. She has sought advice from her friends and tried to think happy thoughts. She argues with herself, frustrated because she knows she is afraid of things that she shouldn't fear. She has tried to relax and she's even given meditation a go. Nothing has really helped, and her anxieties are still getting the best of her. She has finally conceded she needs to meet with a therapist.

Melanie is still breathing a bit heavily as she collapses into a chair in Dr. Smith's office. After a big gulp and deep breath, Melanie details the sense of terror she experiences when she gets in a car. Her fears that she'll have a wreck overwhelm her. She completely gave up driving three weeks ago after she became so anxious on one outing that she pulled over, parked her car, and called a friend to pick her up. She can now only manage being in a car if someone else drives, and even then she feels panic until she gets out. Her heart pounds, she perspires, and she feels as if she is hyperventilating. It's all she can do to get from one place to another, even if someone else drives. Obviously this can't go on. Melanie is embarrassed to keep asking friends to take her to and from work, and she can't even visit her parents across town. Yet, the more she has tried to control her anxiety, the more it has controlled her.

As she fretted about how this initial appointment might go, Melanie wondered what Dr. Smith would do. Would she have to talk about her childhood? It was pretty normal. A history of traumatic auto accidents? Nothing to report here either—only a fender bender in a parking lot years ago. Maybe it's something about her personality that is screwed up. Melanie hopes not. Her twenty-four years have seemed pretty normal until now and she'd hate to think she was such a head case that all the while she has been messed up without even realizing it. Maybe Dr. Smith is one of those counselors who just listens and doesn't really give advice. "Wow," she muses to herself. "I'm even worrying about what my therapist will say. I'm hopeless!"

What direction should Melanie's therapist take? Counselors have a broad range of theories to choose from, and Dr. Smith's choice will make a vast difference in the way counseling progresses—and how well Melanie fares.

What approach might you choose, and why? If you are like many therapists, you have heard of exposure therapy for anxiety, yet you don't know exactly how to use it. It is my hope to help you understand exposure therapy and its cousin, response prevention—both among the most empirically sound techniques available to therapists today—well enough that you are freer to use exposure by itself and in conjunction with other proven therapies for anxiety.

We'll start by briefly examining the common problem of anxiety disorders and the variety of treatment approaches to them. Then we will review some of the reasons that, despite the supportive scientific literature, exposure therapy (ET) and response prevention (RP) are often overlooked by therapists. Despite this oversight, ET and RP constitute viable options, and, as we will see, ET in particular is finding new outlets within the new, third-wave therapies for anxiety.

Anxiety Disorders Are Common

One of the ironies in discussing ET for anxiety is that both the diagnosis and the treatment fly under the radar. Hot topics like bipolar disorder, attention deficit-hyperactivity disorder, and even autism grab media and popular attention. Yet, the truth is that anxiety disorders are the most common group of mental illnesses in the American population (Kessler et al., 2005).

Burijon (2007) concisely summarizes the epidemiology of anxiety disorders, finding that 13 to 18 percent of Americans experience them (Brown, Campbell, Lehman, Grisham, & Mancill, 2001; Zimmerman & Chelminski, 2003). Among those who seek professional care for psychological problems, anxiety is the most common reason (Harman, Rollman, Harnusa, Lenze, & Shear, 2002), with up to a quarter of the U.S. population meeting the criteria for a diagnosis of an anxiety disorder at some point in their lives (Quilty, Van Ameringen, Mancini, Oakman, & Farvolden, 2003). This confirms Clark and Beck's (2010) point that the lifetime prevalence rate for at least one anxiety disorder is consistently 25 to 30 percent in community samples. These data translate to more than 30 million Americans being impacted by an anxiety disorder each year (Rapaport, Clary, Fayyad, & Endicott, 2005). Generalized anxiety disorder alone accounts for 8 percent of the diagnoses in primary care and is the single most commonly diagnosed anxiety disorder (Dugas & Robichaud, 2007). Anxiety is common in young people as well. Literature surveyed by Wood and McLeod (2008) showed rates of high anxiety at 6 to 11 percent in school-age children, though Clark and Beck (2010) cited data showing six-month prevalence rates in minors to be as high as 17 percent. Moreover, childhood anxiety is a gateway condition in that it signals increased risk for a variety of mental illnesses (Britton, Lissek, Grillon, Norcross, & Pine, 2011). None of this data speaks to the common subclinical levels of worry and anxiety that most everyone experiences from time to time.

So Melanie has plenty of company in her suffering. The ubiquity of anxiety means it accounts for much pain, decreased productivity, damaged relationships, and lowered quality of life. There is need for those in the helping professions to continue learning more about anxiety and those who suffer from it. Moreover, it behooves us to use the best techniques science offers—including ET and RP—and so in the pages that follow I will consider certain common assumptions about treatment and why these assumptions mean that ET and RP may be underutilized despite their proven value.

Likely Expectations of Anxious Clients

As psychological problems have become increasingly accepted in our society, people are less hesitant to acknowledge their "issues," but they often respond to popular conceptions of what causes those issues and what to do about them—schemas that may or may not match the science that points mental health professionals to best practices. Let's consider a few of these common assumptions.

Medication

The first professional most people with anxiety consult is a physician, and indeed medication is easily the most common treatment for anxiety (Stein et al., 2004) and the one expected by many sufferers. There is good reason for this expectation, as the effectiveness of medication in anxiety disorders is well documented (Roy-Byrne & Cowley, 2002; Dougherty, Rauch, & Jenike, 2002; Yehuda, Marshall, Penkower, & Wong, 2002). However, being helpful does not make them the best or even necessarily the first choice. The public may not realize this, in no small part because medications are touted as the answer to psychological problems in advertisements aimed at the masses, sponsored by pharmaceutical companies.

But there are several problems with putting a person with anxiety on medication, aside from the usual concerns about expense and side effects. First, medication is not the *only* effective treatment and may well not be the *most* effective (or even the least expensive). Many physicians may default to the prescription pad, not even thinking to weigh medication against psychotherapies and behavioral techniques. This means, in many cases, that the individual enters into a long-term use of the medication as a way of addressing the anxiety. To borrow from the old adage about giving a man a fish versus teaching him to fish, medication is a daily "fish," while cognitive behavioral therapy (CBT), including ET and RP, and its newer relatives acceptance and commitment therapy (ACT) and dialectical behavior therapy (DBT), offer actual "fishing" skills.

If a physician does refer a person with anxiety for psychotherapy, it may be after medication has failed to have the desired result. Yet, this approach leads to a further complication. As we will see, ET and RP rest on the assumption that a fear must be faced to be overcome. If medication takes the edge off of the anxiety, it may work against the habituation necessary to overcome anxiety. If the medication is for "as needed" usage, another complication follows: the availability of the pills can serve as an avoidance or escape option, making ET less effective. None of this is to say, by any means, that medication is not helpful or that it is not necessary in many circumstances. It *is* to say that it likely is prescribed more often than is necessary and can at times compromise the effectiveness of psychotherapy for anxiety.

Physicians often do refer people with anxiety for therapy, and many, like Melanie, seek counseling before turning to medication. There are a variety of psychotherapeutic options available for anxiety—some well supported by evidence, others not so much. Here are some of the most important ones.

Psychodynamic Therapy

The long and rich history of psychodynamic theories has influenced popular thought to a great degree, leading to the common assumption that the roots of fears lie in events from one's childhood. Freud (1920/1966) gave much attention to anxiety disorders and saw them generally as symptoms of repression—and especially of sexual repression. Therapy based on his theories would aim at uncovering what was repressed so as to thwart the need for anxiety as a defense. Recall the classic Little Hans case that Freud (1909/1955) presented. This five-year-old boy developed a fear of horses after he saw a large horse fall and kick aggressively to get up. Freud interpreted this as repressed sexual attraction toward his mother and hostility toward his father, all displaced onto horses. This might be a long, challenging road of therapy.

The various descendants of Freud would take differing approaches to Melanie's situation, perhaps discussing her internal dynamics, or attachment patterns, or object relations, but all might miss the mark, given what we shall see about the nature of anxiety and how it is perpetuated. While there are certain benefits to deep explorations of personality and history, these are often more than is needed to alleviate anxiety. They are, however, often helpful ancillary approaches to address personality change that may be needed in addition to anxiety relief or when anxiety is more complicated.

Supportive Therapy

Many counselors adhere to a supportive or nondirective approach; these therapists are heirs to the pioneering work of Rogers (1957, 1961). Simple in theory but challenging in practice, *nondirective therapy* offers unconditional acceptance and regard as the person shares his or her thoughts and feelings, reflecting these thoughts and feelings back accurately and without judgment. This emotional congruence undoubtedly offers support and comfort to the patient, but both theory and empirical support are lacking when it comes to explaining why this approach would help with anxiety disorders. As we shall see, reassurance seeking often exacerbates anxiety, suggesting that this type of approach might keep the sufferer coming to therapy but is unlikely to alleviate the anxiety. Counselors may be enticed by such an approach, as accurate empathy is indeed basic to doing good therapy, and most therapists are trained in this model in graduate school, making it comfortable for the therapist as well. But the skills of accurate empathy, while necessary, are far from sufficient to relieve anxiety. Talking about her fears may make Melanie feel better, but it won't get her back behind the wheel of a car.

Precipitating Events

Melanie wondered whether she might be asked to retrace an early event that started her fear. There is logic in this approach, which indeed was evident in Freud's Little Hans case (1909/1955), mentioned earlier. Freud obviously looked past the surface possibilities for the explanation; however, a specific incident leading to a phobia is very common and readily explained by a cognitive behavioral model (see, e.g., Clark and Beck's [2010] explanation of Little Hans using two-factor learning theory). Behaviorists, though, trace their understanding of anxiety back to the classic Little Albert experiment of Watson and Rayner (1920), wherein the authors demonstrated that a phobia could be produced via classical conditioning by pairing loud, aversive noises with the presence of a rat, which had theretofore not been feared by the subject. You may recall that pairing a neutral stimulus (a rat, in this case) with an unpleasant one (the loud noise) was shown to cause the subject to become afraid of the neutral stimulus.

There is no doubt that classical conditioning plays a role in the formation of many anxieties, but it is now also clear that those fears are maintained by a different process of negative reinforcement: the elimination of an unpleasant event contingent on a certain response; in this case, moving away from fear is reinforced, thus strengthening the tendency to move away from fear in the future. This accounts for the persistence of fears long after the initial conditioning (Clark & Beck, 2010). However, no clear origin in classical conditioning can be found in many cases. Tryon (2005), for instance, sees it as empirical fact that few persons with phobias recall their having a traumatic onset. Rather, other origins might obtain; for example, a simple anxious false alarm to a neutral stimulus might start the process of forming the phobia (Forsyth et al., 2007). In Melanie's case, she might have incidentally had an anxious thought while driving, beginning the process that led to her seeking counseling. Or, the training may have been gradual or merely the result of a pattern of thinking. The key feature, either way, is the maintenance of the fear through self-reinforcing avoidance and escape behaviors (note that this process has more nuance, as the following chapter will show). Fears may begin with an event, but they are sustained by avoidance and escape (Richard, Lauterbach, & Gloster, 2007).

There are many, many other strategies counselors might use, but the above three (a psychodynamic approach, a supportive approach, and a search for precipitating events) are the most common and the most entrenched in popular understanding. Yet, the core problem found at the heart of most anxiety disorders is a commitment to avoiding feeling anxious or experiencing any unpleasant private event (Forsyth et al., 2007). Thus, whatever the origin of a fear, it is avoidance of experiencing sensations and thoughts of fear that allows the anxiety to thrive. Avoiding anxiety won't eliminate it; only facing it will. This is why exposure therapy works (we'll look closely at the evidence for this in Chapter 2). If Dr. Smith is aware of this, he may need to address and correct Melanie's expectations before introducing her to the concepts of ET.

Some Reasons Why Therapists May Not Choose Exposure Therapy

Clients are not the only ones who enter a first session with preconceived ideas and expectations. Counselors operate within their own systems of assumptions and approaches. Despite the solid theoretical and empirical basis for ET, there are several reasons it is often not chosen by clinicians.

Training, Experience, and Bias

Van Minnen, Henriks, and Olff (2010) offer several critical factors to help account for why therapists may not choose ET for post-traumatic stress disorder (PTSD) in particular, though these are relevant to decisions regarding all anxiety disorders. First, many therapists lack training in and experience with ET. Citing the work of Becker, Darius, and Schaumberg (2007), van Minnen et al. (2010) note that only 31 percent of psychologists surveyed had formal training in imaginal exposure (IE), with their own study confirming this finding. Subjects in the van Minnen et al. (2010) study reported higher rates of training in eye movement desensitization and reprocessing (EMDR) than in imaginal exposure. Other than possibly a brief mention in a course on behavior therapies, ET is not commonly taught in most training programs for mental health professionals, and it is even more unlikely that structured opportunity is provided to practice it under the tutelage of a supervisor with experience in ET. Clearly, training programs need to be more intentional in training in effective therapies such as ET and to offer opportunities to practice these skills. Van Minnen et al. (2010) also found that male therapists are more likely to use ET than female therapists, possibly due to the women seeing it as a less credible and more stressful therapy as compared to the men.

Comorbid Diagnoses

Becker, Zayfert, and Anderson (2004) found that 37 percent of clinicians saw a comorbid diagnosis as a contraindication for ET for PTSD. Certainly other diagnoses must be borne in mind, especially given the propensity for a single anxiety disorder to be accompanied by one or more other anxiety disorders or other mental illnesses. Nonetheless, there may be an inclination to use this tendency as a rationalization to move toward more familiar and rehearsed treatments. Care can instead be given to placing ET within a context of a treatment plan that addresses other issues, rather than omitting it from treatment plans altogether.

Professional and Practical Issues

Many clinicians who might be inclined to use ET still hesitate to use it due to understandable concerns stemming from the typical standards of practice. Most therapists build their schedules around the forty-five to fifty-minute clinical "hour," a long-standing tradition. Third-party reimbursement schedules have grown around this tradition, with procedure codes for psychotherapy generally being focused on fifty-minute sessions. However, many exposure sessions take longer than fifty minutes to accomplish, especially if they take place in the natural environment (for example, meeting someone at the mall who is afraid of public places). This model of therapy conflicts with traditional practices on several fronts.

First, if you use longer sessions to provide for longer and more realistic exposure to feared stimuli (the preferred approach, as we shall see), it can be challenging to plan your schedule around them. Second, insurance companies don't seem to know very much about exposure therapies, and finding a code for a longer session is challenging if not impossible, so getting reimbursed is a challenge. An option is to bill the client directly for the extended session. Clients may have their own concerns with this; it may help to discuss with them the notion that longer exposure sessions now can shorten the course of therapy in the long run. One can hope insurance carriers will come to recognize this as well.

Then there are the logistical issues of ET done outside the office. In addition to scheduling, planning and expenses (such as mileage or public transportation costs and so on) make these sorts of sessions difficult for the therapist. Sensitive legal and ethical issues may come into play around, for example, riding in the car with a client like Melanie to coach her through an exposure. What would it mean if she had an accident in the car with her therapist as a passenger? Or, what if the therapist needed to drive the client? While we'll address these kinds of issues in detail in Chapter 4, observe now how they realistically might discourage therapists from using ET despite its proven effectiveness.

Finally, there is the ethical consideration of potential danger to the client in some exposures. What if, at Dr. Smith's direction, Melanie is driving while anxious and has an accident? Also, by definition in ET you invite clients into perceived danger or threat, making it more likely that they will be unhappy with the treatment you prescribe. While we will consider ways to manage these issues in Chapter 4, they still may tip the scales against ET in the minds of many clinicians unfamiliar with these methods.

Attrition

Most counselors are compassionate, caring individuals who want to help others. But most of us also do this to make a living, and we need clients in order to do that. Clients come to counseling in hopes of feeling better, so while we (and often they) know that sometimes you have to feel worse before you feel better, they may not agree to doing exposures. Rosqvist's (2005) argument—that evolution has made us hedonists and thus resistant to doing things that are uncomfortable, like exposure therapy—may overstate the case, but there is no denying that humans prefer to avoid discomfort and pain. After all, it is this dynamic that accounts for the persistence of anxiety, as people work hard to avoid the discomfort of feeling afraid. While many tout the maxim "no pain, no gain" when it comes to physical exercise, this is a harder sell when it comes to emotional "exercise." So there is a tendency for clients to avoid or drop out of uncomfortable therapies like exposure. The empathetic therapist also may struggle to ask Melanie to expose herself to her fears not only because of Melanie's discomfort, but because of the angst it may cause the therapist as well. Between the prospect of making both client and therapist uncomfortable and the risk of losing the client, it is understandable that many mental health professionals might pass on ET, whether it is effective or not. It is therefore vital for the counselor to understand the "healthy pain" of exposure as a necessary stretch in the road to recovery and to effectively communicate this to the client. We will discuss ways to do this in Chapter 3 and note others in subsequent chapters.

Creativity

Another hindrance to the use of ET is the energy and creativity required to plan and execute exposures. Even when the therapist understands the rationale and strategy for using ET, it requires much customization for individual clients. For example, how do you expose a client to vomit if he is afraid of throwing up? Or how does a person with OCD expose herself to feared thoughts of hurting others? Even for those who see the value in exposure, are convinced by the research, and are willing to use it, frustration may follow when it is a struggle to think up how to expose the client appropriately. Solving this problem is a major focus of this book; Part II offers a storehouse of ideas for addressing many fears.

Neglect

Maybe the most elusive reason ET is not used more often is because it simply is neglected. Whether due to the hindrances discussed above, or the lack of attention in popular media, or simply because therapists haven't read the literature on it, ET is more often overlooked than ruled out. Or as Richard et al., (2007) observe, "It is not so much that exposure therapy is *dismissed* as it is *ignored*" (p. 2; italics in the original). Clearly ET must occur to the clinician as an option if he is ever to actually choose to use it.

DBT, ACT, and the Enhanced Relevance of Exposure Therapies

A theme in this chapter so far is that most clients and therapists aren't really looking for a modality as challenging and effortful as ET. The focus of much of Western psychology has been on a control and mastery approach wherein the individual somehow overcomes problems and gains mastery over them (Forsyth et al., 2007). Westerners want to "beat" anything negative or unpleasant, which may be part of the "hedonism" of the West as described by Rosqvist (2005). Therefore, it is not intuitive to most of us to walk into anxiety-provoking settings if we don't have to, especially with the intent of experiencing and not fighting the anxiety.

However, a group of therapies has emerged in recent years whose practices and tenets aren't tied up in control, mastery, and the aversion to discomfort. Building upon aspects of traditional cognitive behavioral theory and practice and also upon Eastern philosophies and spiritual traditions, these "third-wave" therapies posit that some unpleasantness must be accepted in pursuit of higher goals of living out one's values (Hayes, Strosahl, & Wilson, 1999; Eifert & Forsyth, 2005). (I would add that these approaches also fit nicely in many Judeo-Christian and Muslim traditions.) In the view of these therapeutic approaches, anxiety switches from being a driving force to be avoided at all costs to an unpleasantness that may diminish as one sets one's eyes upon higher goals, or as one simply accepts it (in a positive sense of the term) as part of the inevitable challenges of life.

What does all this have to do with ET? These approaches actually add depth and incentive to traditional ET, giving the challenges of exposing oneself to the anxieties' greater meaning rather than simply ridding oneself of the fear. These approaches place ET in the service of higher ends and goals for life, stressing more of what one is missing due to anxiety rather than merely seeking to alleviate the anxiety. Thus, these approaches provide rationales that overcome hesitancies about using ET. While the more established cognitive behavioral therapy (CBT) can incorporate aspects of this bigger-picture philosophy, there are two major third-wave therapies, DBT and ACT, that I'll introduce here and that will be given more attention in Chapters 6 and 7.

Dialectical Behavior Therapy

Dialectical behavior therapy (DBT) is largely the brainchild of Marsha Linehan (1993a, 1993b, 1995), who built on cognitive behavioral therapy (CBT) by drawing on Eastern influences, primarily the idea of mindfulness described by Buddhist monk Thich Nhat Hanh (1999). The model is based in the idea of being mindful of the present moment, in the sense of accepting each moment nonjudgmentally while experiencing it to the fullest. This practice includes developing skills to tolerate distress—a clear link to exposure therapy, which invites clients to tolerate their distress around a feared item. Developing these foundational skills enables clients to develop other skills to manage and tolerate emotions (*emotional regulation*). While the DBT model was originally developed for use with borderline personality disorder, it has found broader application. Being mindful of the moment is an excellent way of facing any emotion, and anxiety in particular. Indeed, DBT's mindfulness-based emotion regulation skill building is really a form of exposure built into a broader therapeutic approach.

Acceptance and Commitment Therapy

Another of the third-wave cognitive behavioral therapies is acceptance and commitment therapy (ACT). Originated by Steven Hayes (Hayes, Strosahl, & Wilson, 1999), it shares in common with DBT an approach wherein one does not "fight" anxiety, but accepts it in the service of larger goals. Acceptance and commitment therapy flows from functional contextualism as a philosophy of science and from relational frame theory, which is a way of conceptualizing behavior, language, and cognition (Hayes, 2005; both of these concepts will be explored in Chapter 7). It stresses the importance of change at a deeper, broader level than just eliminating unpleasant emotions. Indeed, some negative feelings are accepted as a necessary part of movement toward life goals and as coming with one's commitment to those goals. Anxious avoidance takes one's focus away from larger goals (Eifert & Forsyth, 2005) and hinders progress toward them. Mindfulness plays a role in ACT, too, though ACT takes the concept further in addressing the client's values and purposes. In the philosophy that underlies ACT, life is about more than avoiding suffering, and suffering, including anxiety, often must be accepted to achieve one's goals. Putting coping with anxious thoughts and feelings in the context of the larger goals of life empowers the individual to expose herself to the things that are feared.

These third-generation approaches place ET and RP in the context of a step toward a better life, rather than limiting exposure's usefulness to just the alleviation of anxiety. While certainly a life without excessive anxiety is better than one with it, when ET and RP can help clients move toward a vision of a richer, more gratifying life, they are even more valuable. Practitioners of ACT, DBT, and related therapies stand to gain from a firmer grasp on how ET and RP can enrich these approaches.

CHAPTER 2

Exposure and Response Prevention: The What, How, and Why

In the preceding chapter, I talked about certain challenges and hurdles to using ET. This chapter will answer some basic questions on the nature of ET and its effectiveness in helping anxious individuals. If you are to use the techniques and suggestions later in the book, you will first need to have a grasp of ET and an accurate appraisal of what it offers. I'll begin by tracing the development of exposure therapy and its relatives to give you an idea of the rich history of theory and research that lies behind these therapies, leading up to an understanding of what ET is in its modern form. We will then explore the mechanisms by which ET reduces anxiety, and, finally, we will consider the nature and usefulness of response prevention as the complement to exposure therapy.

What Is Exposure Therapy?

"Exposure therapy" is a term that is applied to the modern heir to certain more basic approaches to treating anxiety—approaches that date well back into the history of psychotherapeutic intervention. "Exposure" may be understood as a common term for the active ingredient in theoretically disparate theories of change (Foa & Kozak, 1986). These theories hold in common the idea that it is therapeutic to expose oneself to aversive or unpleasant situations, objects, or places that one unnecessarily avoids.

Exposure therapy has its roots in behaviorism and behavior therapy. These evolved to include cognitive processes as material for therapy, and the third wave of CBT gives broader contexts for ET. The story of these therapies begins in the early years of psychological research.

Behavioral Antecedents to ET

Several important theoretical and therapeutic predecessors paved the way for exposure therapy as we now know it, including classical conditioning theory, two-factor theory, systematic desensitization therapy, flooding, and implosive therapy.

CLASSICAL CONDITIONING

The basic model of exposure therapy is an outgrowth of one of the most familiar experiments in all of psychology: Pavlov (1927) and his dogs. Pavlov knew dogs salivated at the sight of food, but he noticed that they also salivated at events that preceded the presentation of food. Intrigued, he experimented and found he could train them to salivate at the presence of a stimulus theretofore unassociated with food. If the ringing of a bell coincided with the presentation of food, for example, soon the dogs would salivate at the ringing of the bell alone, regardless of the availability of food. This phenomenon came to be known as *classical conditioning*. The implications of this theoretical model were manifold; one fairly practical sequel was applying classical conditioning theory to explain how particular fears are acquired. That is, if someone experiences fear in the presence of a previously neutral cue, that cue could become what was known as a *conditioned stimulus* for fear.

The presence of classically conditioned fears in humans was established in another famous study, Watson and Rayner's Little Albert study (1920). The subject, a young boy named Albert, was not naturally afraid of a white rat and was allowed to play with one. However, while he played with it, the experimenters made a loud noise behind Albert, causing him to cry. After a few more trials of this, Albert would begin to cry at the mere sight of the rat. He was now conditioned to associate fear with the rat, just as Pavlov's dogs associated the bell with dinner. Applications of this principle abound. A person working in a business with one irritable manager might come to associate being at work with fear of being criticized by the manager, such that the fear persists even when the manager is not in the office. Many children learn to fear a visit to their physician for the possibility of getting injections.

It also is common to see such conditioning occurring in a single trial: one fall down a flight of steps can lead to a fear of heights. In my own experience, one incident of my car overheating in a severe traffic jam led to anxiety for months whenever I approached the intersection where this occurred.

A classical-conditioning understanding of anxiety is rooted in animal models, as are treatment approaches to resolving it. The literature on exposure as a treatment for anxiety in animals is helpfully summarized in Todd and Pietrowski (2007). They conclude that not only does animal research teach us about anxiety, but it supports exposure therapy in treating it—even without a cognitive component. We will return to this idea shortly.

TWO-FACTOR THEORY

The classical-conditioning model is robust to explain fear, especially phobias, but it proved inadequate to explain why just a few or even one learning trial could lead to anxieties that lasted for years (Barlow, 2002). There had to be something else to sustain fears over time or to explain how in many cases they worsened as years went by. Enter O. Hobart Mowrer (1953, 1960) and his two-factor theory. Endorsing the earlier view of classical conditioning as the mechanism by which fears and phobias were created, Mowrer postulated that fears were then maintained through a separate and subsequent *operant conditioning* process wherein one learns by being active, or "operating," in ways that lead to reward or punishment. Once a person is conditioned to fear a particular thing, place, or situation, approaching it creates anxiety. While ostensibly this serves an adaptive function of warning the person about a dangerous environment, it also encourages the person to avoid the feared stimulus (an avoidant response). The person therefore acts to avoid the feared object or situation and thus decrease the unpleasant sensations of anxiety—basically a process of negative reinforcement (wherein one's reward for a behavior is escape from an unpleasant situation). Here is where the need for response prevention arises: it basically addresses this second, operant factor. By preventing the escape or avoidance behavior, response prevention undermines the negative reinforcement part of the pattern and weakens the rewarding impulse to evade anxious feelings.

When the feared situation is not truly a threat, avoidance deprives the person of the chance to disprove the anxious feelings and discover that the situation is safe after all. Returning to the example of my overheating car, I indeed experienced anxiety as I approached the intersection where the crisis occurred, but necessity compelled me to drive through it nonetheless. After a few such exposures to the intersection, the fear disappeared, as this reality testing showed that the protective goal of the fear was no longer necessary. In contrast, had I yielded to my fearful feelings and avoided the intersection, my avoidance would have relieved my anxiety through a process of negative reinforcement. The discriminative stimulus (nearing that intersection) associated with the original (classical) conditioning would evoke distress, and escaping from that stimulus would be rewarding in itself (the negative reinforcement aspect of operant conditioning, where my *action* yields the reward). Two factors, then, would strengthen my anxiety around the intersection, and the anxiety would persist.

Richard et al. (2007) posit three reasons that the two-factor theory might explain the efficacy of ET. First, fear should *extinguish* (gradually subside) in the absence of a paired *aversive stimulus* (that is, when one experiences the situation without experiencing something bad), just as mine did when I continued to drive through the intersection. Second, facing and staying in the feared situation prevents avoidant responses (a factor in favor of using response prevention therapies); the individual now learns new information about the situation—that it is no longer dangerous. Third, when facing a genuine threat, people generally do not remain anxious indefinitely, so that being exposed in session may create an anxiety that diminishes during the session or before the next one.

While the two-factor theory proved popular over the couple of decades after its proposal, problems came to light, which are nicely summarized by Clark and Beck (2010). First, the presumption of classical conditioning that any neutral stimulus (one that signals neither reward nor punishment) can become associated with an unconditioned stimulus was not supported by studies showing that some stimuli could be more easily conditioned than others. For example, it was easier to train subjects to fear snakes than flowers. Second, not all phobias have a clear learning history rooted in a traumatic event: recall that Melanie has never been in a major auto accident yet fears causing or being in one. Third, evidence suggested that fears could be learned vicariously, by merely observed upsetting events. Fourth, many who experience trauma do not develop associated fears, leaving scientists to wonder why some do and others don't. Clark and Beck's fifth and final concern is that the two-factor model fails to explain the epidemiology of phobias, exemplified by the fact that many more people experience the pain of dental work than are bitten by snakes, yet fear of snakes is easily the more common of the two. Richard, Lauterbach, and Gloster (2007) add that many individuals who experience aversive events and acquire fear responses do not engage in avoidant responses, even if their fear does not remit. Others continue escape and avoidance behaviors despite no longer reporting feeling fear in the situation. In the end, the two-factor model may provide some insight into phobias, but it is inadequate to explain the range of fears, particularly those that are diffuse and relational.

The two-factor theory has been important in developing techniques and spurring research. It even has some explanatory value for why ET works, but its numerous weaknesses have left it as more of a historical springboard for research than a viable contemporary theory upon which to build clinical practice. Nonetheless, it addresses an issue that remains vital: "the manner in which problematic fears and anxiety are maintained over time is more relevant to treatment than are the origins of those fears" (Abramowitz, Deacon, & Whiteside, 2011, p. 36).

SYSTEMATIC DESENSITIZATION

Drawing from the classical-conditioning model above, Joseph Wolpe (1958, 1961, 1990) was most influential in developing a therapeutic technique to use these behavioral processes to reduce anxiety. *Systematic desensitization* is concisely summarized by Head and Gross (2008) as

> the process by which a person is induced into a deeply relaxed state and is presented with a series of graduated anxiety-evoking situations using imaginal, also known as in vitro, exposure. When anxiety is experienced during exposure, the image is terminated and a relaxed state is induced. With continued exposure to each situation, the person's level of anxiety weakens progressively, until the person no longer experiences anxiety in response to the aversive stimuli. (p. 542)

Head and Gross (2008) provide a concise outline of the steps in systematic desensitization. First, the client is taught relaxation skills to reduce bodily tension, typically by sequentially tensing and relaxing muscle groups until the entire body is relaxed. The next step is to develop a hierarchy of situations that evoke anxiety, ranging from mild to severe. For Melanie, simply thinking about sitting in a stationary car might be a lower-level situation, while actually imagining driving would be much higher. Since systematic desensitization relies more on imaginal exposure, actual driving likely would not be included in the hierarchy. Once the hierarchy has been developed collaboratively with the client, the next step is imaginal exposure. Once the client is relaxed while visualizing a neutral scene, then the lowest item on the hierarchy is presented by verbal description. The client imagines it for a few seconds, and a rating is taken of the anxiety. The same scene is tried until it is experienced with lowered anxiety, at which point therapist and client proceed to the next most difficult item, and so forth, until the client is comfortable imagining the highest item on the hierarchy.

Wolpe (1958) saw *reciprocal inhibition* as explaining the effectiveness of systematic desensitization, the idea being that experiencing a response antagonistic to the anxiety while imagining it will cause the suppression of the anxiety response. While the mechanism of action is still debated, Tryon (2005) has affirmed that systematic desensitization is one of the most empirically supported treatments available, though Head and Gross (2008) note that it is now used more often in formats other than Wolpe's, with certain elements being incorporated into exposure therapies and other CBT approaches. For example, as early as 1981, Walker, Hedberg, Clement, and Wright applied the concepts to in vivo exposures, allowing clients actually to approach the fear-producing stimulus itself, not merely imagine it. However, a milestone report by Marks (1975) gave evidence that relaxation itself was not necessary; the graded exposure was the critical variable in promoting change. Importantly, this article was the origin of the term "exposure therapy." As is true of many therapies, we know they work, but we struggle to find the precise mechanism that leads to the change. Nonetheless, the basics of systematic desensitization continue to inform current exposure therapies.

FLOODING AND IMPLOSIVE THERAPY

Two other important threads in the ET story stem from classical conditioning. Both flooding (Miller, 2002) and implosive therapy (Levis, 2002) have empirical support as treatments of anxiety. *Flooding* can be briefly explained as an all-out approach wherein the patient quickly confronts her most feared situation, imaginally or in real life, while minimizing escape from the provocative context—engaging in response prevention (Abramowitz et al., 2011).

Flooding is built on the classical-conditioning tenet that "the repeated presentation of an emotionally conditioned stimulus (CS) in the absence of a biological unconditioned stimulus (UCS) will lead to the extinction of the conditioned response (CR; the 'symptom')" (Levis, 2008, p. 272). Unlike other exposure-based therapies, flooding begins with highly anxiety-evoking stimuli rather than working up to them (Zoellner, Abramowitz, Moore, & Slagle, 2008), either imaginally or in real life. For example, in Melanie's case, Dr. Smith would "flood" her by immediately having her drive until her anxiety relented. This procedure theoretically would lead to the extinction of her fear response.

Implosive therapy also works from the idea of extinction of a response and is a variation of flooding. Stampfl and Levis (1967) distinguished it from flooding by using only imagined scenes, but these scenes were grossly exaggerated or improbable (if not impossible), so that even more anxiety was evoked until it essentially imploded in the process. This might entail Melanie imagining witnessing auto accidents or having close calls herself. Finally, implosive therapy adds a psychodynamic element by directly appealing to sources of anxiety, such as rejection, death wishes, and so on, that are seen as core fears in the human personality.

Systematic desensitization, flooding, and implosive therapy all have proven effective, and the common core for all is exposing the client to fear-evoking stimuli while simultaneously inhibiting or prohibiting escape and avoidance (Abramowitz et al., 2011). Thus, not only is fear unlearned, but safety is relearned by preventing the client from responding by escaping and encouraging him to sit with his discomfort in exposure. These therapies set the stage in the 1970s and 1980s for the development of the kinds of exposure therapies we will be examining shortly.

The Role of Cognition

Cognition earned a place in behavioral approaches as it became clearer that human behavior is greatly influenced by patterns and content of thought, and as new research methods allowed us glimpses into the unobservable realm of thinking. None of the approaches considered thus far actually addressed the role of thinking in anxiety or its cure, unless you consider imagery in exposure or in relaxing visualizations to be cognitive in a sense. The cognitive view offers a more powerful and straightforward account of how cognition, feeling, and affect all contribute to human suffering (Forsyth et al., 2007). Cognitive approaches stress the ways that memory, attention, irrational beliefs, and untenable self-statements and other maladaptive thoughts are important in explaining and treating mental disorders in general and anxiety disorders in particular. As Reading (2004) explicated, many human emotions are due to our ability to think about the past and future, and anxiety is generally focused on excessive mental apprehension about the future, even in the absence of precipitating events that might incline us to be excessively apprehensive. Thus, the dominant model in the tradition we are considering is no longer behavior therapy, but cognitive behavioral therapy (CBT). The section below briefly reviews some aspects of thinking processes that contribute to the development and maintenance of anxiety; we'll consider the role of these in exposure therapy.

Inappropriate Thinking

The notion that changing anxiety must include changing faulty thinking dates back at least to Beck (1979), though the errors in cognition may take a variety of forms. Several of them are summarized by Abramowitz et al. (2011); these include maladaptive beliefs and biased information processing.

MALADAPTIVE BELIEFS

Since anxiety is often an irrational fear, one naturally would suspect sufferers to experience irrational thinking, or *maladaptive beliefs*. Such beliefs exacerbate anxiety by either encouraging avoidance of anxious situations or excusing escape and avoidance behaviors, thus building resistance to exposing oneself to anxious situations. Several types of errors in thought processes are comprehended here, including overestimating the probability of bad things happening. While Melanie is right in that any time one drives there is some chance for an accident to occur, her completely refusing to drive reflects an exaggeration of that realistic concern and a distorted idea of the odds. A similar distortion may involve the exaggerated consequences one might fear should something negative happen. For example, despite its being a normal and typically healthy function, people who fear vomiting may overestimate how bad it would be if they actually *did* vomit. Some may even fear they wouldn't be able to stop vomiting and thus would die. While vomiting is far from a pleasant experience, it is not bad enough to warrant this level of fear. Overestimating the odds of bad things happening and holding exaggerated ideas of the consequences are beliefs that don't fit reality and thus serve to perpetuate anxiety in unhealthy ways.

Another of the maladaptive beliefs summarized by Abramowitz et al. (2011) is an inability to tolerate uncertainty about the future, even regarding events with extremely low objective probabilities. People with such beliefs are not willing to accept even the slightest chance a feared disaster might take place. This sort of illogic may also lead people to struggle to accept that routine aches and pains are just that, given the remote possibility they signal cancer or another dreaded disease. Others suffer from an extreme underestimation of their ability to cope should a feared event materialize. Those who fear vomiting, for example, may do so in part because they fear they would not be able to cope if they should start to vomit. Finally, some anxious persons actually fear the symptoms of anxiety themselves, a phenomenon dubbed *anxiety sensitivity* (Taylor, 1999). This phenomenon is common in panic disorders and represents almost a feedback loop wherein the person becomes anxious, reacts to the anxious sensations with increased anxiety (such as fearing a heart attack will come of the anxiety, or fearing embarrassment if anxious in a public place), leading to heightened symptoms and so forth. Here the anxious symptoms are seen as threatening in themselves, often because they are not understood or are misunderstood. We will see that the physical symptoms can be addressed with interoceptive exposure approaches, though the cognitions behind them must be corrected as well. Response prevention as well may be applied to situations where a client is avoiding feelings, not just places or situations. We will see that sometimes even some cognitions are escape behaviors to which response prevention needs to be directed.

BIASED INFORMATION PROCESSING

Cognitions are not just the words we say to ourselves in our heads, but also other mental processes that might lie outside our immediate awareness, including some of the ways we process information, with anxious persons often experiencing what Abramowitz et al. (2011) call *biased information processing.* They note two basic forms for this: selective attention and selective memory.

In *selective attention*, anxious persons pay more attention to stimuli that relate to their concerns. A person who fears becoming ill will be more attentive to minor aches and pains, while someone afraid of storms will be more likely to watch the sky for darkening clouds. Besides the obvious inconvenience in attending to these supposed signs of danger, the tendency to do so makes the world in general seem to be a more threatening place.

Selective memory is a tendency to remember things that are consistent with distorted thinking related to fear. Melanie might, for example, tend to recall accidents she has seen in the past or news spots reporting on auto accidents. With the recollection of more adverse scenarios, the fears are confirmed and thus heightened.

A Cognitive Model of Anxiety

Clark and Beck (2010) draw on years of cognitive research into anxiety to offer a model of the cognitions that result in anxiety. Central to the model is the notion of *vulnerability*: a sense of being subject to dangers, both within and outside the individual, over which the individual lacks control or for which there is an inadequate sense of safety. Cognitive distortions, as discussed above, exacerbate this tendency so that a person senses danger easily and feels inadequate to cope with it. This all leaves the person feeling vulnerable and thus anxious.

The authors' model has eight central tenets. *Exaggerated threat appraisals* mean that the person is sensitized to any signs of personal threat, giving enhanced and selective attention to things that might have a negative impact. Anxious persons also have a tendency to see themselves as lacking in coping resources, resulting in *heightened helplessness.* Moreover, persons inclined toward anxiety may miss or misconstrue information in the environment signaling safety, what Clark and Beck (2010) call *inhibitory processing of safety information.* This will play a role also in the need for response prevention, as we will see.

The anxiety process itself hijacks more constructive types of thinking such as logic and realistic appraisal, leading to *impaired reflective thinking.* The cognitive processes contributing to anxiety are not only problematic, but virtually automatic or reflexive, making it seem to be uncontrollable. Here Clark and Beck (2010) find an important place for ET, given that simply controlling cognitive processes may prove inadequate. Anxiety may seem to be uncontrollable due to the mixture of *automatic and strategic processes* underlying it. The automaticity of cognitive processes enables a more profound activation of threat-based cognition, but exposure allows the person to garner disconfirming evidence for the high threat value he places on the feared object or situation. Automatic thoughts may lead to automatic escape behaviors; response prevention interventions help disrupt this nearly reflexive process.

Next, the model sees a *self-perpetuating process*, where the self-focused attention due to signs and symptoms of anxiety creates even more anxiety about being anxious. Unlike ET, the Clark and Beck (2010) model argues for *cognitive primacy* in anxiety—they see both the appraisal of the primary threat and the secondary threat of perceived vulnerability as being essentially cognitive. Finally, enduring, core beliefs that tend toward susceptibility to anxiety yield a heightened and ongoing *cognitive vulnerability to anxiety*. So, while finding a place for ET and RP in disconfirming anxious cognition, Clark and Beck's model is indeed predominately cognitive in its understanding of anxiety and its treatment.

We will see that while CBT is considered the treatment of choice for anxiety disorders (Barlow, 2002; Forsyth, Fusé, & Acheson, 2008), we are still in doubt about how exactly it works. A closer examination of this issue will shed light on the processes of CBT, but it will also point us toward the third-generation approaches of acceptance and commitment therapy and dialectical behavior therapy.

How Does Exposure Therapy Work?

Before we review the empirical evidence that ET works, we'll explore how—by what mechanism—it works. For all the studies demonstrating ET's effectiveness, there is still some mystery surrounding exactly *how* it works (a failing typical of research that demonstrates therapeutic effectiveness). A seminal article by Tryon (2005) presented an authoritative critical review of the literature on potential mechanisms of ET, and I will use his outline for my survey of potential explanations and their support (or lack thereof), building on the preceding survey of ET's development and examining which rationales hold up and which fare less well.

Reciprocal Inhibition and Counterconditioning

We encountered the notion of reciprocal inhibition in the discussion of Wolpe's (1958, 1961, 1990) systematic desensitization, with the theory being that a relaxed physiological state is incompatible with anxiety and thus inhibits it. While several studies cited by Tryon (2005) support using relaxation in desensitization (Davison, 1968; Kass & Gilner, 1974), others have not found it necessary (Miller & Nawas, 1970; Nawas, Welsch, & Fishman, 1970). Tryon concludes that the weight of the evidence does not support deep muscle relaxation as promoting reciprocal inhibition; that is, the incompatible state of relaxation is not necessary to reducing anxiety.

Wolpe (1958) also used the concept of *counterconditioning* to explain the long-term benefits of systematic desensitization. The basic idea is that one replaces an old response with a new one; this is essentially the behavioral equivalent of reciprocal inhibition (Davison, 1968). Marks's (1975) review found no difference between systematic desensitization and graded exposure. Plus, the effectiveness of flooding and implosive therapy also argue against the relaxation component being necessary, so Tryon concludes the empirical evidence does not support counterconditioning as a clear explanation of the benefits of exposure.

Habituation, Extinction, and the Two-Factor Model

Habituation is the decrease of a response due to repeated stimulation, so it might be argued that repeated exposure habituates the anxious person to the anxious stimulus. Tryon's (2005) review showed that there are some such effects in ET and systematic desensitization, but that habituation, being rather temporary and reversible, cannot explain the longer-term changes in response strength and thus is unable by itself to account for the effectiveness of those therapies. *Extinction* attributes the decreased response to the lack of reinforcement, whether positive or negative.

Rosqvist (2005) argues that negative reinforcement is more powerful than positive reinforcement and thus can account for the second factor of the two-factor theory. Whereas *positive reinforcement* is the receipt of a positive consequence upon engaging in a certain behavior, *negative reinforcement* is the elimination of an unpleasant stimulus contingent on engaging in a certain behavior. For example, a mother is negatively reinforced when she concedes the candy bar to her tantrumming toddler at the grocery store checkout. By giving in, she resolves the embarrassing and irritating situation. Rosqvist's take on the second factor argues that a process like negative reinforcement is at play in maintaining anxiety, as avoidance or escape behaviors are negatively reinforced by reduced anxious arousal. This makes ET a form of extinguishing the anxiety by not reinforcing it through escape or avoidance. Repeated failure to surrender to the demands of anxiety makes it likely the unpleasant circumstances will die out and thus remove the second of the two factors. Yet, Tryon (2005) notes that there is no clear causal mechanism for the extinguishing of anxiety, so Rosqvist's view allso falls short as an full explanation of cause. The evidence that classical conditioning (the first factor in two-factor theory) is not always present in fear learning further undermines two-factor theory as the prime causal mechanism of anxiety.

Cognitive Changes

Tryon (2005) also surveys the data on cognitive factors that might account for the effectiveness of ET given that humans are awake and active during the process of exposure and thus are experiencing cognition. As described above, anxious persons may *expect* worse to happen than is likely should they face certain events. Facing the fear might offer new data and a change in expectation—in other words, cognitive changes. This may occur to some extent, but literature reviewed by Tryon did not yield a satisfactory theoretical explanation for why it might be so.

Other cognitive factors that might account for positive change through ET are increased *sense of self-efficacy* and *cognitive restructuring.* Self-efficacy would increase because, by the person's intentionally encountering something he has long avoided, he learns he can face challenges successfully. Cognitive restructuring is a staple of CBT in both Beck's model (Clark & Beck, 2010) and the rational emotive behavior therapy of Ellis (Ellis & Blau, 1998). It entails the therapist working with the patient to uncover irrational cognitions and restructure them; for example, to see a feared object as less dangerous. Here, too, though, it is the case that even though these therapies seem to work, no clear mechanisms of change are evident.

Tryon's Model

So what *does* account for the change that results from exposure therapies? Tryon (2005) proposes a model of memory mechanisms that learn, noting that learning and memory are affected and driven by experience. Thus, memory is dependent on sensation and perception.

Tryon argues for a three-layered neuronal network where one layer receives stimulus inputs, the second forms concepts from these, and the third represents the resulting behavior. Experience forms a synaptic architecture among these levels that can be altered by processing that cascades through the levels. In other words, experience lays down a pathway among these levels of processing (stimulus, concept, behavior), much as walking repeatedly across a field of grass creates a trail.

The cascade of processing may be initiated by exposure to a feared stimulus. Exposure to a feared stimulus creates a dissonance within the neuronal structure as it currently exists, interrupting the movement from stimulus to concept to the normal behavioral output. But the structure seeks consonance between internal states and external environments (thus, the calming after being exposed for a while). Each exposure experience recreates the pattern of dissonance moving to consonance, and in so doing changes the connection weights in the network, affecting behavior, cognition, and emotion until the fear states are reduced.

While Tryon acknowledges the model has some weaknesses, it is a cogent fundamental explanation of neuronal changes that occur in exposure. In the pages that follow, I will largely avoid discussion of underlying mechanisms and use a terminology of "change" in a figurative rather than a literal sense. So, for example, while I may say that avoidance behaviors are negatively reinforcing of anxiety, I concede that this may be an imprecise depiction of the actual processes Tryon (and others with related models) are attempting to describe at a more fundamental level. Stated differently, I will stick to more psychological explanations of the changes wrought by exposure, while assuming there are relevant underlying neurological correlates.

Explaining Exposure: Toward the Third Wave

Thus far we have traced what exposure therapies are and how they may work. Exposure therapies are a subset of CBT, which is still the gold standard (Barlow, 2002) for treating anxiety. There is, however, room for improvement. For all of the good CBT can do, it usually does not "cure" anxiety, nor does it help everyone who receives it. Often short-term gains are lost as time goes by. Forsyth et al. (2007) note some of the shortcomings of CBT.

First, CBT tends to cast the symptoms as the problems, a mistake therapists may share with patients who see anxiety in this way. But anxiety is not just a problem in itself; it also impairs the quality of life for the sufferer as she most often has "a more important life to be lived behind the symptoms" (Forsyth et al., 2007, p. 74). Second, Forsyth et al. maintain that we need a more process-oriented approach than is suggested by defining the problem as "anxiety." That is, they suggest the processes that turn normal anxiety into major problems should be the target of treatment. Third, they argue that the anxiety disorders are overall more similar to one another, and overlap more, than is often thought; the evidence for this is in how the same or very similar treatments are helpful across the spectrum. Moreover, avoidance and escape behaviors are similar across the family of anxiety disorders.

Fourth, Forsyth et al. (2007) observe that there is considerable overlap between anxiety and other mood disorders. This observation leads Barlow, Allen, and Choate (2004) to argue for a modular approach to mood disorders: combining CBT approaches in a way that addresses the core features of these disorders while allowing therapists to pick and choose relevant components. (Chorpita's [2007] book exemplifies a modular approach with children.)

Potentially most importantly, Forsyth et al. (2007) observe that CBT treatments are almost always designed to help clients control and master their anxious symptoms, which is largely the typical expectation for clients when they come into therapy—and for many therapists as well. While this might be reasonable, the authors maintain (and I agree) that the larger issue is to live a more meaningful life. One might manage to control anxiety but not have a larger sense of meaning; or one might have a sense of purpose and meaning that leads one to accept a certain amount of anxiety in pursuit of higher goals. On the latter point, the authors refer to the newer generation of psychotherapies, including acceptance and commitment therapy (ACT), that aim beyond merely learning to control anxiety toward accepting a degree of anxiety as part of working toward meaningful goals.

A study by Karekla, Forsyth, and Kelly (2004) showed that subjects had lower attrition rates when ACT-enhanced CBT was used versus traditional CBT. In particular, rationales that promoted controlling the experience of panic versus directly suppressing panic, and living more fully versus merely controlling panic, led to lower attrition rates and higher buy-in for exposure therapies. Similarly, dialectical behavior therapy (DBT; Linehan, 1995) stresses being in the present over conquering the anxiety itself. We will examine DBT and ACT in detail in Chapters 6 and 7.

The future of CBT approaches would appear to lie less in better strategies for overpowering anxiety and more in managing anxiety, particularly in the context of higher life goals. Exposure therapy, when used in the context of these third-generation cognitive-behavioral-based therapies, is put in aid of allowing clients to endure and manage their anxieties so as to move toward a better quality of life. This rationale will prove vital in overcoming resistance to ET (both our own and our clients'), enhancing compliance, and helping clients toward a richer existence.

Empirical Support for Exposure Therapy

To this point we have asserted that ET and its treatment partner, RP, are effective. But demonstrating the effectiveness of a treatment is extremely important—perhaps never more so than today. All parties—clients, therapists, and third-party payers—look to science for the most effective and efficient treatments, inspiring a movement toward empirically supported treatments (ESTs) (see Rosqvist, 2005, for a discussion of this trend). To be considered to have clear empirical support, techniques must fare significantly better in randomized clinical trials than control conditions. A plethora of studies support ET; maybe the best concise review of these is found in Abramowitz et al. (2011). The authors accurately note that many of the studies available use broader approaches than just ET (mostly variants of CBT); this makes sense as, in practice, the two groups of therapies (ET and CBT) overlap. What follows is a brief summary of their work.

Exposure therapy is most commonly seen as a treatment of specific phobias, often used in conjunction with cognitive techniques. While the literature shows ET to be effective in phobia treatment, cognitive techniques do not enhance its success (Wolitzky-Taylor, Horowitz, Powers, & Telch, 2008). Exposure therapy is also effective for panic disorders, in particular the agoraphobic component of these. Exposure therapy and response prevention, in the combined form often called exposure and response prevention (ERP), are useful in treating obsessive-compulsive disorder (OCD), an encouraging find given that OCD was considered resistant to psychotherapy until the 1960s. The response prevention piece is especially critical, as it addresses the compulsions of OCD by discouraging the use of rituals as a way to decrease the anxiety of obsessions. Even hypochondriasis, which is not grouped with anxiety disorders in DSM-IV, is helped by ET, as is health-related anxiety, with the few studies on this generally including ET with broader CBT approaches.

Post-traumatic stress disorder (PTSD) has been widely researched using ET and is a focus of Foa's (e.g., Foa et al., 2005) model of prolonged exposure therapy (PE), which will be discussed in Chapter 8. With PTSD, the goal is to expose the sufferer to fear-evoking memories or cues that are associated with the original trauma and that elicit anxiety on an ongoing basis. Abramowitz et al. (2011) conclude that CBTs that incorporate exposure activities are highly effective in decreasing symptoms of PTSD. While these authors cite research on the effectiveness of eye movement desensitization and reprocessing (EMDR; Shapiro, 1995), they note that studies show that ET is effective with or without the eye movements, which would make EMDR just another form of exposure.

Social phobia (or social anxiety disorder) is responsive to ET, with or without cognitive restructuring, and even generalized anxiety disorder (GAD) can be helped by ET when specific fear-provoking stimuli can be identified. Indeed, the best treatment effects for GAD were found when both cognitive and behavioral elements were included. Abramowitz et al. (2011) note that the American Psychiatric Association recommends exposure-based CBT as a first-line treatment for OCD, PTSD, and panic disorder when the patient prefers therapy over medication.

It is clear that ET has found the attention of many researchers, whose work has shown it to be vital in treating the gamut of anxiety disorders. Response prevention has been applied successfully to a variety of anxiety-related disorders in adults and children (it was first used by Meyer in 1966), though its use is mostly associated with OCD (Franklin, Ledley, & Foa, 2008). When therapists explain the rationale for using RP to their patients, it enhances compliance and encourages patients to take steps to prevent certain avoidance behaviors and face their anxiety. In the next chapter, we'll start learning how to use exposure therapies, beginning with response prevention.

CHAPTER 3

Exposure Therapy's Partner: Response Prevention

It is an axiom of treating anxiety through exposure that the only way out is through. Melanie's fear of being in a car has led to her refusal to drive and to virtual paralysis even with someone else driving. There is no "magic fix" whereby she will wake up one day and be able to drive without anxiety. She must drive while feeling anxious, exposing herself to the situation she fears. But to do so, she will actually have to drive. That will mean that she must not continue responding to her fear by avoiding traveling in a car. Dr. Smith will not succeed with Melanie until he guides her away from—that is, works with her to prevent—these escape and avoidance responses.

While response prevention (RP) is not always a necessary component in treating anxiety, it is often a very helpful complement to exposure therapy. In fact, Richard et al. (2007) observe that most forms of exposure include a component of RP. So, before turning our attention to the specifics of implementing exposure therapy (ET), we will examine the function of escape and avoidance behaviors and offer guidance on assessing these in anxious clients. We then consider a rationale for why and when RP should be used, present practical steps in implementing it, and close the chapter by discussing how RP is integrated into ET.

Escape and Avoidance in Anxiety Disorders

Healthy anxiety serves an important purpose: discouraging us from approaching things that might hurt us. This wonderful defense is evident from infancy. The classic "visual cliff" experiment of Gibson and Walk (1960) was intended to demonstrate depth perception, but actually assessed a natural fear of heights. Most infants in that experiment opted not to crawl out onto a safe plate of glass when they perceived a "cliff" beneath it, even with their mother urging them on from the far side of the glass. We are born with a vigilant protection system.

But anxiety disorders are just that—disorders—and reflect a protective system gone awry, causing us to be fearful when there is no need. And just like with warranted fears, the visceral impulse is to avoid or escape situations that evoke the unpleasant feelings of anxiety. It works, too, for obviously one is never hurt by avoiding a perceived danger, real or not. The sense of control such behaviors give a person make them even more powerful (Mineka, 1979) and harder to surrender; the person attributes his safety to the avoidance behavior rather than to the fact there was no danger.

Avoidance and escape are negatively reinforcing, conforming to the second part of Mowrer's (1953; 1960) two-factor theory as discussed in Chapter 2. While we saw that the two-factor theory is inadequate to explain all anxiety disorders, negative reinforcement still plays a critical role in much anxiety, though nowadays a cognitive component is often presumed to be a factor as well (Barlow, 2002). Almost all major theories of fear converge at the point of seeing avoidance or escape behaviors as part and parcel of the fear response (Barlow, 2002). Avoidance and escape are twins that work together to keep the person from being exposed to a feared object or situation: avoidance by keeping the person away and dodging anxious feelings altogether, and escape by moving the person away from the apparent danger and associated feelings. In so doing they deprive the person of the opportunity to learn that there is actually nothing to fear, and consequently they perpetuate the anxiety.

Exposing oneself to a feared situation requires not only overcoming the fear itself, but resisting the pull of immediate relief promised by avoidance. Response prevention was first utilized in conjunction with ET in the seminal work of Meyer (1966); it involves the intentional curtailment of any avoidant or escape reactions. Stated differently, RP is preventing responses that allow the anxious individual to escape from or avoid anxious feelings. If one does not evade the anxiety, one must face it, and thus exposure occurs. Only then does one learn experientially that there is indeed nothing to fear.

Pathways to Escape

Both avoidance and escape behaviors serve to keep the individual "safe" from the supposed threat heralded by anxious thoughts or feelings, and thus they can be called *safety behaviors*. These are any internal or external actions by an individual that function to keep her away from a perceived danger. An *internal action* might be, for example, imagining one is somewhere else or thinking about something other than the fear; an *external action* might be, for example, Melanie's refusal to drive a car. There is some nuance to the exact thought, situation, or experience that is avoided in these behaviors across different anxiety disorders. In general, three paths may be taken to escape anxiety: learned fears, compulsions, and interoceptive conditioning.

Learned Fears

In Chapter 2, we saw there is a basic classical-conditioning aspect of many phobias: it is clear that a frightening run-in with a potentially dangerous object or situation can leave a person fearful of that same or a similar object or situation in the future. A child who is bitten by a dog may thereafter have a fear reaction at the sight or sound of a dog and may avoid dogs in the future. Many fears (most often the phobias) can be traced to a specific origin—the dog bite—where they were learned. Specific fears such as these are often simpler to treat, even responding in some instances to one intensive session (Öst, 1989). This is, in part, owing to the circumscribed nature of the fear and the limited avoidance and escape behaviors that are available. In any event, the person cannot successfully conquer these fears if he continues to avoid the feared object or situation. The person who fears dogs will have to be willing to take a walk in the neighborhood, even though dogs may bark or run by.

Compulsions

Obsessive-compulsive disorder (OCD) functions rather differently than most anxiety disorders. Thoughts become stuck on certain fears and exhaust the sufferer as he wars against these worries, trying to resolve them. Often the resolution comes in the form of a compulsion, a behavior that serves to relieve the tension of the obsession, if only very temporarily. Best known among these patterns is obsessing about germs. The individual will fret about the ubiquitous presence and danger of germs and may then take recourse to washing her hands to be cleansed of the dreaded germs. This produces immediate relief (a pattern of negative reinforcement), initiating a sequence that may be repeated hundreds of times per day.

Another variant of compulsions in OCD is *magical behavior*. While washing hands logically does get rid of a few germs (though the resultant dry skin may be more vulnerable to germs), some obsessions do not have such a logical outlet. For example, if you fear you might accidentally do something that will harm a loved one, no simple behavior can allow you to avoid that event. Often the person with OCD will somehow invent a solution that is purely based on "magic." He might turn a light switch on and off four times and thus avert the disaster. To an outsider, the illogic is obvious, as it is to the person with OCD in calmer moments. But if flipping a light switch a few times can make the anxious feelings recede—if only for a few minutes—then it seems worth it. In exposure therapy for OCD, RP would serve to stop the switch-flipping—the magical cure—while the person is exposed to the anxious thoughts and feelings.

Compulsions can also be mental, not just behavioral (American Psychiatric Association, 2000), and can include, for example, counting to four in one's mind, praying silently, or mentally repeating words or phrases. Mental compulsions are most challenging to address in that they are always convenient and are not subject to monitoring by others. The individual is on her own in her efforts to prevent these compulsions.

Finally, some compulsions serve not to reduce specific obsessions, but to give the world a "just right" feel. These compulsions may border on obsessions and tics (Radomsky, Bohne, & O'Connor, 2007), but still serve to decrease anxiety or arousal. A person may feel compelled to straighten, order, or balance things in his environment. Here the implication is that a level of anxious feeling or unrest irritates the person, prompting him to seek the relief of symmetry. Response prevention focuses on avoiding taking actions to make things "just right" so as to expose the individual to the anxious feelings.

Interoceptive Conditioning

Interoceptive conditioning refers to learning associated with physical sensations of anxiety arising within oneself. These sensations are of critical concern with panic disorder in particular, though they are manifest in many other types of anxiety. DSM-IV-TR (American Psychiatric Association, 2000) lists these symptoms as indicative of panic attacks: palpitations (or pounding heart or accelerated heart rate), sweating, trembling, sensations of being short of breath or smothering, feeling as if one is choking, chest pain or discomfort, nausea or abdominal distress, dizziness (or feeling lightheaded or faint), paresthesias (numbness or tingling sensations), and chills or hot flushes.

In many cases these sensations simply accompany fear as part of the fight-or-flight response, but in others these feelings themselves further frighten the individual and become something to be avoided in themselves. Barlow (2002) notes that often in panic disorder there is no clear cue for the fear reaction, with the person apparently just reacting to these symptoms. If the symptoms are not properly understood (and often even if they are), the person may fear they signal a serious illness or event such as a heart attack, creating a vicious feedback loop and resulting in a panic attack. Agoraphobia, for example, is the avoidance of open spaces prompted by the fear of a panic attack in public or away from safety. The response of staying away from, or leaving any situation where any interoceptive signal is aroused, must be prevented to allow exposure to these sensations and thus to their elimination. We will revisit interoceptive exposure in Chapter 4, but for now note that RP may be a needed cotherapy with ET in cases of panic disorder.

In all instances of avoidance and escape behaviors, the negative reinforcement and misattribution of what actually prevented the feared event strengthen the tendency to use the strategy again. In so doing, the anxious individual is deprived of the opportunity to disconfirm the association of danger with the object. Melanie, by not driving eases her anxious feelings, but also increases her tendency to blame them on the danger of driving, and keeps herself from the experience of driving enough to recognize that it is indeed safe. These actions thus exacerbate the anxiety and pose an obstacle to exposure. Response prevention can help.

When to Consider Response Prevention

Many, if not most, anxieties will involve some type of escape or avoidance behaviors, and left unattended these may undermine formal exposure exercises (Wells et al., 1995). It is thus an important aspect of any assessment to consider whether avoidant responses are evident. Ritual or response prevention is most commonly used with OCD (Franklin, Abramowitz, Kozak, Levitt, & Foa, 2000). Response prevention actually enhances the positive effect of ET (Foa, Steketee, Grayson, Turner, & Latimer, 1984), nearly doubling gains compared to the use of ET alone. Done well, ET/RP is superior even to treatment of OCD with serotonin reuptake inhibitors (Simpson & Liebowitz, 2006). Franklin, Ledley, and Foa (2008) summarize research to show that exposure with response prevention has demonstrated efficacy in patients of all ages, from children to older adults, and in outpatient settings as well as controlled clinical trials. They note that it has also been helpful with hypochondriasis, body dysmorphic disorder, eating disorders, substance abuse disorders, and Tourette syndrome. They argue that the literature may contraindicate RP for patients with personality disorders, due to poorer outcomes, though they say this does not mean it is ruled out with this population. Comorbid Axis I disorders do not significantly preclude the effectiveness of RP, either, though very high levels of depression lessen its effectiveness. In general, Clark and Beck (2010, p. 251) conclude that "response prevention can be an important treatment component for any of the anxiety disorders." Thus, I argue that it should be routinely considered whenever ET is used, and deliberately included or excluded based on the following guidelines:

1. If comorbid disorders on either Axis I or II are present, is the anxiety disorder primary? (If not, you may need to focus on the more pressing disorder.)
2. Is the diagnosis OCD? (If so, RP with ET is the gold standard treatment, each component improving the effectiveness of the other.)
3. Are there specific triggers for the anxiety that is the target for ET which the client actively avoids or escapes? Triggers for the anxiety may be external situations—settings, or persons—or internal—thoughts, feelings, or other sensations.
4. Does it appear that the client will have difficulty exposing herself to the target fear because of the potency of the escape and avoidance behaviors?

If the first question is answered "no" and any of the other three merits a "yes," then RP should be considered as part of ET.

Identifying Escape and Avoidance Behaviors

Clients will vary greatly in their awareness of safety behaviors, just as the content of the behaviors themselves will vary. "For exposure to accurately target a fear, the complex constellation of fear cues and contexts needs to be understood" (Powers, Smits, Leyro, & Otto, 2007, p. 112). It is imperative, then, that the therapist take sufficient time to understand the contexts and cues associated with anxiety before instituting response prevention and/or exposure. There are three steps to cover in this assessment process: educating the client on the nature and function of safety behaviors; developing a detailed list of his safety behaviors; and identifying triggers for these behaviors.

Educating the Client

The therapist may begin by explaining to the client that it is characteristic of excessive anxiety to try to avoid whatever evokes the anxiety. She might say something like this:

> Normally, anxiety serves us by keeping us away from danger. If you see a venomous snake, you draw back almost automatically. If you know snakes are in a certain part of a wood, you may avoid going there. This is good, for you clearly don't want to be bitten. But problematic anxiety causes a person to move away from or avoid situations or things that are not dangerous in reality. You don't really need to avoid, say, an elevator, as they are safe and most everyone can ride them with little or no problem. But a person with problematic anxiety might use the stairs or find professionals who have offices on the first floor so as to dodge the feeling of being in or even near the elevator. Now think about [the client's fear]. When you get near the thing you fear, what things do you do to get away? And what things do you do to simply avoid it? These are examples of safety behaviors that actually make your fears persist in troubling you. Our goal will be to help you avoid doing these behaviors so as to help your mind and feelings learn that the thing you fear isn't really dangerous.

This will introduce the client to the types of behaviors that RP will target, but more detailed explanation will likely be needed. It's important that you clarify to the client that safety behaviors are any mental or physical actions that serve to keep a person from a fear or reduce the anxiety that a person has by seeking escape rather than facing the anxious thought or situation. Guide the client to understand the two major categories of safety behaviors (avoidance and escape) and the nature of safety signals. *Avoidance behaviors* are physical or mental actions that seek to keep the individual away from the perceived threat (and therefore "safe"). Offering your client a variety of examples may help. Physical avoidance behaviors might include:

- not eating foods that one feels or believes will make one sick
- staying away from shopping malls if one is afraid of public places
- avoiding movie theaters, religious services, or concerts for fear of being in a crowd
- not visiting a friend in the hospital for fear of catching an illness

- staying with an unpleasant job due to fear of having a job interview
- playing video games for long hours to avoid troublesome thoughts
- deliberately thinking about irrelevant things to avoid worrying about something
- not driving for fear of having an accident

You might suggest one or two avoidance behaviors common to persons who have your client's particular anxiety and ask the client to give you an example or two to ensure that she understands the idea. Basically, these are things that prevent the experience of anxiety.

Escape behaviors are any mental or physical actions intended to reduce or eliminate anxiety once it is evoked. Compulsions fall into this category, as they serve to decrease the anxiety associated with obsessions or general anxious arousal. If the client has obsessions, then you might explore the things he does to decrease the anxiety caused by obsessing. If explicit obsessions are not apparent, then you might explore the things he does to decrease arousal, from straightening objects to controlling a conversation. In some cases, substance use serves as an escape from anxious thoughts and feelings.

Another form of escape behavior is *reassurance seeking.* This is seen in OCD and GAD particularly, and it takes the form of asking others questions to seek confirmation that one is okay. For example, a woman worried about her health might ask a friend if her breathing sounds normal, or a man worried that he may have sinned might ask his religious leader for affirmation that he has not. In these cases, the person is negatively reinforced when another person assures him that his worry is unwarranted. Like other compulsions, this only serves to perpetuate the worry after brief moments of relief. A similar pattern is evident in those who seek reassurance by searching the Internet for information on their symptoms to affirm that they are not life threatening.

Finally, escape behaviors are about getting away from situations or items perceived as dangerous. Here again, the anxiety comes with approach, but rather than accept it and move on into the situation, the person with anxiety may retreat and escape. Melanie, for example, might come near her car and hold the keys in her hand, then begin to feel anxious. She has learned to see driving as dangerous through experience, and her interpretation of experience, so it is easiest for her to do what eases her body's danger signal. So she walks away and cancels the appointment to which she was headed. The relief is instant, and it's addictive, as it confirms her interpretations and strengthens the relationship between avoidance and relief so that next time will only prove more difficult. Escape behaviors can be subtle, as people may move away from perceived dangers sometimes without even realizing it; for example, a person with social phobia may look down or even cross the street to avoid a passerby.

A final category of safety behaviors is *safety signals* (Abramowitz et al., 2011). These are not actions, but cues in the environment that decrease anxiety by their mere presence, though in reality they do nothing to decrease danger. These can be places (like home), or people (staying close to a friend, or having one's MD on speed dial), or objects (such as p.r.n. medications for anxiety, or carrying a motion-sickness bag). These cues are misconstrued as protecting the person from feared consequences that are, of course, more feared than they need to be. Like the other safety behaviors, they offer some temporary relief while unintentionally serving to perpetuate the anxiety or worry. As such, these are "responses" that need to be prevented to facilitate full exposure to the pathological anxiety. If they remain, they will weaken the effectiveness of ET. For instance, if a person with panic disorder carries emergency medication with him, he will not be completely on his own in exposing himself to the interoceptive symptoms of panic. To overcome anxiety, safety signals need to be let go.

Part of an early interview with the client should include questions about potential safety signals; these might range from carrying hand sanitizer to keeping antacid in one's purse to only going with a friend to the mall. To some extent, this is how Melanie can cope with being in the car: if someone else is driving, the other person signals safety from her own driving.

Developing a Detailed List of Safety Behaviors

To maximize the effectiveness of ET, a good response prevention strategy will be important. Once the client has learned the basics of what safety behaviors are, and how they function to maintain anxiety, she is ready to look more closely at her own life and at how these come into play.

As you guide your client through the explanation of escape behaviors, several examples of these will become evident for her. Gentle exploratory questions about her life and habits will likely bring more escape behaviors to light. The education section above offers a good framework to help the client reflect on and delineate more of the ways she keeps herself "safe" from her anxieties.

Equipped with this new knowledge, the client with anxiety will be more cognizant of how anxiety functions in his life and hopefully more aware of safety behaviors. The Safety Behavior Log (Form 3.1), found at the end of this chapter, offers a homework exercise to assist the client in observing and monitoring safety behaviors. Ideally, the client would use it for an entire week to cover all situations faced in the course of normal life. Compliance with this schedule may prove a challenge, so doing it well for two or three days may work better. The goal is for the client to pay very close attention to safety behaviors, and a couple of days of good observations is often better than an entire week of spotty data.

As the counselor, you might fill out part of the form as you do the educational piece so that the client sees how to use it. The instructions are fairly simple: record escape behaviors as you notice them (a partner or friend may help, since escape behaviors are often automatic); record each instance and bring the form to the next session. When the homework is returned, you can review the information with the client and help him evaluate whether these behaviors actually were helpful and whether he is beginning to see how the behaviors actually perpetuate anxiety rather than help it. This pivotal insight is necessary to prepare the client for the actual RP intervention and also in helping identify triggering events or situations that will be important in planning ET.

Identifying Triggers

Triggers are events, settings, people, or thoughts that seem to light the fire of worry or anxiety. For Melanie, just getting near a car can trigger her anxiety, but over time merely thinking of being in a car may be all it takes. She might even begin to feel a bit anxious if she sees a car cruising down the road in a television commercial. This anxious alertness would be a healthy thing if it were signaling genuine danger; for example, when I lived in the San Gabriel Mountains, I learned to react to anything that sounded like a rattlesnake, as they were common in that area. But to react to nondangers is a problem. By understanding what triggers the anxiety, a client can learn even better what he is doing to avoid and escape anxiety and have a better idea of where and when therapeutic exposures may be most effective.

The Tracking Triggers form (Form 3.2) found at the end of this chapter is a simple form that can be used to follow up on the Safety Behavior Log (Form 3.1). Once the client has returned the log, discuss the situations she noticed during the week and help her identify triggers after you explain what they are. Triggers may take three primary forms (Abramowitz et al., 2011): internal, external, or thought triggers. *Internal triggers* are the interoceptive feelings discussed above. Being a little winded after climbing up several flights of stairs might trigger anxiety about having a heart attack, or feeling any sensation in the stomach could trigger a fear of throwing up and start an episode of anxiety or panic. *External triggers* are generally easier to spot. They are any thing or situation in one's environment that cues up anxiety. The rattle I heard in the grass cued up anxious feelings appropriately, but Melanie should not feel anxious watching an automobile commercial on television. *Thought triggers* can be worries coming to mind (signaled by their ubiquitous "what ifs"), or obsessions, or simply thoughts of feared situations or objects. Memories might also trigger anxiety; Melanie, for example, might recall being in a fender bender when she was younger. Doubts about oneself or things important to one, images popping into mind that are upsetting, or impulses to do things one should not are often triggers in OCD.

Again, use the explanation of these categories to help the client survey his own situation, and then have him monitor triggers during the week on the Tracking Triggers form (Form 3.2). Knowing the client's triggers helps the therapist plan where exposure therapy may be needed and alerts the client to when and where he needs to implement response prevention to take a stand against escape behaviors.

Implementing Response Prevention

With a detailed account of specific safety behaviors and an awareness of the triggers for these, the client is ready to participate in response prevention. But, as Franklin et al. (2008, p. 448) warn, "it is completely unrealistic to simply tell patients to stop engaging in rituals" in the case of OCD; this is also true of other safety behaviors if other anxiety disorders are the focus of treatment. As we have seen, these behaviors serve a purpose that is adaptive in the short run. So RP should be implemented with thought and preparation.

Relation of RP to Exposure Therapy

We saw earlier that RP is the partner of exposure therapy. If the anxious person does not engage in any safety behaviors, by default she will be exposing herself to the feared situation. Exposure therapy thus requires RP in a sense, as anxious persons almost always live a life committed to avoiding and escaping their fears, doing what they can to avoid the very thing the therapist will ask of them: exposing themselves to the anxiety. This chapter logically precedes Chapter 4 on how to conduct exposure therapy in that one must stop avoiding before exposure can occur, but in reality they are implemented together. The counselor will do well to have the client educated and equipped for exposure *before* implementing RP, as eliminating escape behaviors means the person is left experiencing the anxious thoughts and feelings. It is important that the client understand that by preventing these responses, she will be left to encounter the feelings without the usual route to resolution. It is important that this fact not surprise her and that her understanding of it set up the context for exposure.

Logically, RP should be implemented only when the therapist believes the client is at a place where he can tolerate the anxiety if deprived of the usual escapes. In many, if not most, cases, proceeding to RP would follow the therapist's developing with the client a strategy for coping with the feelings (the strategy will vary depending on the broader therapy model being used). The RP intervention would then be followed in session by exposure exercises that allow the client to gain experience and a modicum of confidence in his ability to manage anxiety in the real world.

Using Friends and Family

Response prevention (and exposure therapy as well) is a challenge to the client. Persevering through very strong negative feelings is counterintuitive, and it's hard. This is not to mention the struggle just to be aware of triggers and escape opportunities as they arise. For example, one of the challenges to stopping smoking is that lighting up is almost automatic to many smokers, and having to catch oneself before smoking complicates simply stopping. Response prevention is similar in that catching oneself prior to the act is a challenge over and above staying with the anxiety.

Because of this, friends and family are often invited to help the client prevent his responses. Rowa, Antony, and Swinson (2007) note that the literature does not universally support the need for family support, but confirm that overall it is preferable when the family is understanding. Franklin and Foa's (2002) literature review corroborates this conclusion, particularly when the client is from a culture that values family. Studies by Grunes, Neziroglu, and McKay (2001) and Van Noppen, Steketee, McCorkle, and Pato (1997) present data that show superior outcomes when family members are included in exposure and response prevention for OCD in particular.

Clark and Beck (2010) wisely note that in some instances (particularly agoraphobia) a certain friend or family member may actually be a safety cue, and this possibility needs to be considered before involving that person in the RP.

Rowa et al. (2007) offer guidelines for family members and friends that include being educated about the OCD or anxiety, being supportive but not helping with avoidance, being aware that during RP and ET the person is *supposed to* experience anxiety, and knowing not to push the client beyond what she is ready for. While family members can alert the client to safety behaviors and provide encouragement and support through RP and ET, they are helpful only when they are, well, helpful, which sometimes and in some families they are not.

Partial vs. Full Response Prevention

Another critical issue in implementing RP is deciding whether to prevent all responses simultaneously or do so more gradually. Concurring with Rowa et al.'s (2007) conclusion based on the available research, Abramowitz et al. (2011, p. 116) conclude "the optimal response prevention strategy is to instruct the patient to drop all safety strategies at once, 'cold turkey.'" The therapist does well to consult with the patient to determine if he is ready for such a drastic change, and must also make sure a good assessment and instruction have been given to maximize the chances of success.

If the therapist and client agree that total RP is not realistic, then steps can be introduced in two ways. First, therapist and client will target specific safety behaviors or rituals that appear to be good candidates for success and arrange these in a hierarchy. Success with these can then be a stepping-stone to more challenging safety behaviors, moving gradually up the hierarchy.

Another approach is to begin disrupting the rituals or safety behaviors in some way (Summerfeldt, 2008). In OCD, this might mean delaying washing one's hands if one is anxious about germs, or counting more slowly or to a different number if one has a counting compulsion. Assurance-seekers might limit the number of times they ask if something is okay. For Melanie, Dr. Smith might ask her not to check bus schedules or look for jobs only within walking distance. These changes can serve to give some initial sense of success to the client, though care must be taken lest these also morph into new safety behaviors (such as by frequently altering the number to which one counts).

Reviewing the Rationale for RP

During the assessment of safety behaviors, much of the rationale for RP will have become evident to the client. However, before sending the client out to begin RP, it is wise to reiterate the rationale for it (Clark & Beck, 2010). Here are a few key points to cover:

1. Review how the current strategies are not succeeding in overcoming the anxiety and how they can in fact worsen it due to the nature of avoidance conditioning.
2. Specifically, go over the individual's safety behaviors (per the assessment discussed earlier) and show how each reifies rather than remedies the fear.
3. Stress that anxious feelings and thoughts are "false alarms." I often illustrate this point by having the client recall having nervous feelings when watching a movie. In the excitement, one *feels* nervous but at a different level *knows* one is watching a picture projected on the screen in a cinema. The fears in anxiety are a bit like that: they appear and feel real, but deep down you know they are not. But unlike the movies, where you stay with the feelings until the resolution at the end of the film, in real life escape behaviors cause you to miss the way it all works out in the end.
4. Warn the client to expect higher anxiety (Clark & Beck, 2010). Like a wave, anxiety will rise before it lets you back down. In preparation for RP it is important for the client to expect the feelings to worsen and to know that this is expected, natural, and temporary. Remind the client that interrupting the anxiety before it quells naturally will not result in relief and may actually strengthen it.
5. Progress is valued over perfection. It is likely there will be slips where the person engages in the safety behavior. By acknowledging that some of these will happen, the therapist can prevent the client from feeling he has failed and encourage him to carry on despite the setbacks.

Challenges to Response Prevention

While RP is efficacious, it is difficult, and it's even more challenging to compliance than ET (Riggs & Foa, 2008). Whereas exposures are often planned and even guided by a therapist who is present, RP requires the client to be vigilant and ready to resist rituals and safety behaviors at any given moment—and most often she must do so alone. So not only does RP share some of the key challenges of ET—including dropout, refusal, failures, and slips—it may actually be *more* challenging. Response prevention may be even more intrusive upon daily life (Riggs & Foa, 2008) given the ubiquity of triggers, the demands of daily activities, and the unpredictability of the average day.

Here is where a good therapeutic relationship, the support of others, and a solid understanding of why the client is being asked to do hard things will undergird her during these challenges. The best steps for better physical health involve resisting tempting foods and persevering with tiring and even tedious exercise, but we agree physical health is worth it. We would not expect mental health to be improved without similar challenges. Response prevention and exposure therapy are demanding, but, as with diet and exercise, the results are well worth it.

Form 3.1 Safety Behavior Log

Safety Signals

Safety signals are little things you may do, or things you may keep, that give you the feeling of being safe from things that seem dangerous (even though, as you've learned, they may not really be as dangerous as you feel they are). An example would be carrying a rabbit's foot for "luck" to protect you from being robbed. Think about safety signals you use; write down as many as you can think of below; then pay attention to yourself for the next week (or whatever period you and your therapist decide is appropriate) and add any that you notice. At this point, there is no need to do anything about these; just practice noticing them.

Safety Signal	What It Is Supposedly Helping
______________________	______________________
______________________	______________________
______________________	______________________
______________________	______________________
______________________	______________________

Avoidance Behaviors

These are things you do in order to stay away from people, places, situations, things, or even thoughts that make you nervous, anxious, or uncomfortable. Examples might include shopping over the Internet because the mall is frightening (this is an example of a "behavioral avoidance behavior"), or watching too much TV just to keep worry away (this is an example of a "mental avoidance behavior"). Think about any avoidance behaviors you may use, and list as many as you can now. Then spend the next week (or whatever period you and your therapist decide is appropriate) tracking how many times you catch yourself doing the behavior. You may discover ones you hadn't thought of as you go along, so add those and track them as well. Once again, you are only being asked to track these behaviors; changing them will come later.

MENTAL AVOIDANCE

What I Do	What I Avoid By It	(Day/Time) D/T	D/T	D/T	D/T	D/T	D/T

BEHAVIORAL AVOIDANCE

What I Do	What I Avoid By It	(Day/Time) D/T	D/T	D/T	D/T	D/T	D/T

Escape Behaviors

Escape behaviors are things you do once you notice feelings or thoughts of being anxious or worried. The function of escape behaviors is to get you away from what is provoking your feelings or thinking. For example, if you walk too close to the railing on the second floor of the shopping mall and start to feel uneasy, you move farther from the rail so you feel "safer" and less likely to fall. Escape behaviors may also include things like asking for reassurance if you are worrying. Think of the escape behaviors you know you use, and write them down. Keep track of them, and add others as you discover them during the week (or whatever period you and your therapist decide is appropriate).

What I Do	What I Avoid By It	(Day/Time) D/T	D/T	D/T	D/T	D/T	D/T

Compulsive Behaviors

Compulsions, or compulsive behaviors, are mental or physical actions that serve to give temporary relief from anxious or unsettled feelings. Doing them makes you feel better, but the anxious feeling tends to come back fairly quickly. These include things like washing your hands excessively if you're worried about disease, or opening and closing a door five times to ease a worry about hurting someone. Some of these behaviors are not in response to worries, but serve to ease discomfort by giving a sense of control over something (like straightening the books on a shelf until they're "just so"). Think of the compulsive thoughts and behaviors you know you use, and write them down. Keep track of them, and add others as you discover them during the week (or whatever period you and your therapist decide is appropriate), but don't worry about changing them at this point.

Compulsive Behavior or Thought	(Day/Time) D/T	D/T	D/T	D/T	D/T	D/T

Form 3.2 Tracking Triggers

Triggers are thoughts, feelings, or situations that unleash anxiety like the trigger on a gun does a bullet. Triggers can be thoughts in your mind, including worries, memories, unwanted images, doubts, or fears. They can also be situations in your life that provoke anxiety, such as seeing a needle if you are afraid of injections—sometimes even seeing one on TV can kindle anxious feelings. Finally, physical sensations may trigger anxiety. For example, a minor twinge in the chest area might trigger anxiety about your health. The more you and your therapist know about what triggers your anxiety, the better your treatment will work. Monitor one or more of your anxieties over this week (or whatever period of time you and your therapist agree upon) and see whether you cannot find several triggers for each. Don't try to change your response to the triggers; that will be addressed later.

Anxiety #1: ______________________________

Thoughts

a. ______________________________

b. ______________________________

c. ______________________________

Feelings or sensations

a. ______________________________

b. ______________________________

c. ______________________________

Persons, places, things, or situations

a. ______________________________

b. ______________________________

c. ______________________________

Anxiety #2: ______________________________

Thoughts

a. ______________________________

b. ______________________________

c. ______________________________

Feelings or sensations

a. ______________________________

b. ______________________________

c. ______________________________

Persons, places, things, or situations

a. ______________________________

b. ______________________________

c. ______________________________

Anxiety #3: ______________________________

Thoughts

a. ______________________________

b. ______________________________

c. ______________________________

Feelings or sensations

a. ______________________________

b. ______________________________

c. ______________________________

Persons, places, things, or situations

a. ______________________________

b. ______________________________

c. ______________________________

Anxiety #4: ______________________________

Thoughts

a. ______________________________

b. ______________________________

c. ______________________________

Feelings or sensations

a. ______________________________

b. ______________________________

c. ______________________________

Persons, places, things, or situations

a. ______________________________

b. ______________________________

c. ______________________________

CHAPTER 4

Implementing Basic Exposure Therapy

Exposure therapy is really more of a technique than a model of therapy. It is typically considered a behavioral therapy and placed under the umbrella of cognitive behavioral therapy (CBT). But ET need not be seen as merely a CBT technique; it may exist as a group of interventions independent of an overarching theoretical framework. Briefly, exposure therapy "involves deliberate and planned exposure to a feared stimulus, or representation of the stimulus, until the intensity of a person's distress recedes to a level that is (1) lower than pretreatment levels and (2) acceptable to the client" (Richard et al., 2007, p. 4). At a rudimentary level, that is all there is to it. Barlow (2002) traces the move in clinical practice from systematic desensitization to exposure as data emerged suggesting the relaxation component (used in systematic desensitization) was not really necessary and that exposure alone yielded positive outcomes over a number of studies.

Basic ET alone is effective, but its overall effectiveness may be enhanced by contextualizing it within a broader treatment framework or adapting it to various diagnoses: we'll do all this in subsequent chapters. In this chapter we will survey the core processes of ET as well as a basic method of using it in outpatient counseling—that is, if Dr. Smith decided to use it in Melanie's case, this is how he might go about it.

Before we proceed, a note on contraindications is in order. Exposure therapy may not be right for all anxious people. Tolin and Steketee (2007) note that there is not a literature that clearly delineates when ET should not be used, though some clinicians have seen exposure as too stressful for some patients. Some have seen it as too risky for patients who pose a serious danger to themselves or others, or if a comorbid dissociative or psychotic disorder is evident. It may also be too risky when severe anxiety is present.

The clinician is encouraged to exercise professional judgment before recommending ET, weighing the broader issues behind the anxiety. Psychiatric disorders are notoriously interrelated, and a good initial assessment should look for a range of diagnoses before seeing a person's problem as "just anxiety." Moreover, even if the therapist recommends ET, it is not guaranteed that the client will be prepared to cooperate with it. A clear and compelling rationale is needed to enhance buy-in from the client before beginning ET.

A Rationale for Exposure Therapy

If persons with anxiety manage to face their fears and overcome their safety behaviors, they will not end up in a therapist's office in the first place. "It follows that an integral part of any cognitive or behavioral treatment is the presentation of a sound, well-explained rationale for why the client should engage in these particular treatment strategies" (Rowa, et al., 2007, p. 83). Moreover, Rowa et al. maintain that research suggests the client's acceptance of the rationale can enhance outcomes.

Creating a Context for Change

Therapy does not happen in a vacuum, and success with ET depends in large part on what Abramowitz, Deacon, and Whiteside (2011) call "nonspecific factors," which include "variables such as motivation for change, the expectation of improvement, and a warm therapeutic relationship" (p. 49). Often clients have tried a variety of strategies to overcome their anxiety before coming to therapy, or before being open to a challenging approach such as ET. Hope and motivation may be at a low ebb. Standard therapeutic skills of empathy and support are prerequisites to ET; a good treatment relationship must be built first.

In addition to a skillful and optimistic presentation of the rationale for ET, and an adequately developed therapeutic relationship, I find it helps to invoke hope and vision by having the client imagine life when the anxiety is overcome. Elaborate on this with her until she can almost feel a better life. This leads directly into a discussion on the negatives that follow from the anxiety. As the client becomes more cognizant of the poorer quality of life caused by her fears and worries, her motivation to change can improve. In short, do not overlook the basics of good therapeutic technique. What follows is a three-point rationale for presenting ET to your clients.

1. How You Got This Way

This may be the least important point of the three for the implementation of ET, though it is important for clients. Barlow (2002) details ways that fear is learned, but also finds that anxiety need not be merely, or primarily, a learned thing. Jerome Kagan (Kagan & Snidman, 1991) identified a shy and timid temperament that is evident in infancy and often persists as the child grows (Pfeifer, Goldsmith, Davidson, & Rickman, 2002), showing that anxiety can be in a sense endemic for some individuals or that there may be a *diathesis* (predisposition) making them vulnerable to developing clinical anxiety. One need not have had a specific trauma or fear-inducing event to have an anxiety disorder. As we have seen, anxiety problems have much more to do with what *sustains* them than with what *caused* them (Abramowitz et al., 2011). Some clients may appreciate taking some time to explore any roots of current problems, and this process may enhance rapport and possibly provide some helpful insight; however, the past is not the target of ET.

2. How You Stay This Way

Since ongoing responses to anxious feelings and cues perpetuate the anxiety and thus account for its chronicity, it is vital that the client understand this process. This understanding allows the client to see how exposure works and how it will help.

FIGHT OR FLIGHT?

Anxiety does not feel good—which, of course, is the whole idea. Humans, like other animals, are endowed with mechanisms to alert us to danger and motivate us to either attack the threat or get away from it. This is accomplished by activation of the sympathetic nervous system, which in turn underlies most of the physical sensations associated with anxiety.

Sapolsky's (1998) playful explanation of the fight-or-flight response is one I often use to explain the physical symptoms of anxiety and their purpose. Zebras, in his story, live a placid life—until a lion appears by the watering hole. Seeing this very real threat, the zebras' sympathetic nervous systems kick into gear. Fighting is not an option, so they flee. Running recruits blood flow to muscles and away from digestion, possibly leading to nausea, vomiting, or defecation. Breathing and heart rate accelerate, symptoms common in panic disorders. If the lion stops pursuing, the zebra's parasympathetic nervous system takes over, the anxious symptoms subside, and the zebra is back to its peaceful life.

The zebra story serves to educate clients about the physiological aspects of anxiety, neatly separated from the cognitive aspects (since zebras do not think in the ways people do). It also shows the natural function of anxiety and fear: to alert us to and facilitate our escape from imminent danger—and then to subside. In anxiety disorders, anxiety is chronically provoked by things that are neither genuine nor imminent dangers, and due to our ability to think, our fear response can arise at the mere thought of the feared item and persist for much longer than nature intended. One can even become anxious about the feelings of anxiety. The disorder lies in being anxious about things that are not actually threatening.

HOW ESCAPE HELPS

Escape—whether the danger is real or imagined—also brings a physiological reward, as it reduces the autonomic arousal of anxiety and brings us back to a state of peace and calm. Thus, escape is negatively reinforcing. For the zebra, autonomic arousal is the aversive stimulus, and escape is the behavior. When a situation stirs anxiety, finding safety away from that situation is rewarding as it eliminates the unpleasant arousal. This pattern of negative reinforcement serves to train the individual to avoid situations where danger has been encountered in the past (the zebra may feel anxiety as it approaches the watering hole). If those situations continue to pose genuine danger, this may be good. But generalize the danger too much, and the anxiety itself becomes a problem.

HOW ESCAPE CAN HURT

Thirst may overcome the zebra's anxiety about the watering hole, and it may return there. If it does so a few times without incident, the danger signals will diminish and over time it will approach without anxiety. But if it continues to obey its anxiety and avoids the watering hole, its aversion to the spot will increase. Similarly, having experienced fear in the car, Melanie now associates the car with the fearful feelings. As she approaches it, the feelings increase; when she escapes back into the house the anxiety subsides. But there was never a real danger in approaching the car; Melanie simply had the feelings and associated them with the car. (There are cognitive processes that exacerbate this, as we'll see in Chapter 5.)

Efforts to avoid experiencing the unpleasantness of anxiety are labeled *experiential avoidance.* Persons with varying problems with anxiety will seek to avoid unpleasant experiences both in the environment and in their minds. For example, persons with OCD often try to escape unwanted thoughts by supressing them (Abramowitz, Whiteside, Kalsy, & Tolin, 2003). But trying to suppress the anxious thoughts only leads to more.

Experiential avoidance of external experience also fails to help the person with anxiety. The safety behaviors described in Chapter 3 exemplify experiential avoidance, and while they offer immediate relief, it is temporary. Moreover, repeated avoidance of places or things associated with anxious feelings only strengthens the autonomic response when one nears them. This pattern makes it harder to face the stimulus for anxiety and thus to overcome the anxiety.

Another danger with experiential avoidance is that it prevents the person with anxiety from having a disconfirming experience. If one is too anxious to ever ask a question in class, he will never have information to rebut his feeling that the teacher will laugh at him. Experiential avoidance also leads to errors in thinking about what makes one safe. In the above example, the student will conclude that he was not laughed at by the professor because he did not ask a question, strengthening the fear that the professor *would* laugh if he asked a question.

A final consequence of safety seeking is that it easily leads to the belief that anxious feelings will not stop until one escapes. This is supported as the sensations heighten if escape is delayed, creating even more urgency for escape. Now the individual not only fears the situation, but fears that by his being in it the bad feelings will not subside, even if the danger does not prove real. There are, then, a number of ways in which experiential avoidance actually sabotages the individual and perpetuates the anxiety. Given that stories can enhance understanding, Rosqvist (2005) offers some helpful metaphors to communicate to a client how escape and avoidance perpetuate anxiety; you may wish to consult his book for these.

In contrast, repeatedly experiencing anxiety without escaping will lead to a reduction in anxiety; this process is called *habituation.* If you eat your favorite meal every day, you will soon become accustomed to it and your craving for it will wane. It is similar with anxiety: being in an anxiety-evoking situation until the anxiety subsides, and doing so repeatedly, leads to a reduction in anxiety. This is the crux of exposure therapy.

3. How You Get Better

At this point, the counselor might wish to confirm with the client that she understands how current behaviors and mental actions are actually perpetuated by avoiding the experience of the anxiety and thus not having the opportunity to discover that the danger is not real. Many persons with pathological anxiety will acknowledge that their worries and fears are irrational or unnecessary, but they have not *experienced* safety in the midst of them, and thus the anxiety persists. Cognitive assent to a realistic appraisal of actual dangers is necessary, but not sufficient.

As therapy begins, the therapist confirms that the actual danger is minimal, though usually not zero. For example, there is always *some* risk in driving, but there is no reason Melanie's risk should be higher than the average person's. In some cases the risk is indeed zero (such as the person with OCD who thinks someone might die if he does not perform a certain compulsion), but that is the exception.

The counselor can now introduce the basic strategy of ET: exposing oneself to the feared stimulus long enough for the anxiety to subside. Sometimes the person can simply be exposed directly to a feared situation, but more commonly she will be guided through a hierarchy of levels from less anxiety-evoking to more so. For example, a person afraid of ants might first simply listen to the word "ants," then move on to read the word "ants," look at pictures of ants, look at videos of ants, be in the same room as ants, watch the therapist let an ant crawl on his hand, and ultimately let the ant crawl on her own hand. The key is to expose oneself until the sympathetic arousal begins to yield to the parasympathetic calming. When this is accomplished over a number of trials, habituation, the first goal, will take place. That is, the fight-or-flight response will not be evoked when encountering the stimulus; or if it is, it will be mild enough for the person to stay in the situation and not escape to "safety." The client will also overcome a related aspect of anxiety: the fear that the anxiety will not abate unless she escapes from it (Foa, Huppert, & Cahill, 2006).

Expressed colloquially, exposure is "putting your fear to the test" (Abramowitz et al., 2011, p. 109). It is not merely "unlearning" a pathological association of the stimulus and the fear response, but it is "new learning" (Richard et al., 2007, p. 3) or "safety learning" (Abramowitz et al., 2011, p. 48). The client does not just find release from a former pattern, but learns afresh that the formerly feared situation, object, place, or thought is indeed safe. If the client will do the work, a refreshing view of the world as a safer place is the reward.

The dual objectives of habituation and safety learning thus drive exposure therapy. The challenge is that the client must face her anxiety. The therapist needs to be certain that the client understands that the therapy entails facing, and *feeling*, anxiety without trying to run from it (Clark & Beck, 2010). Should the client state that she already faces her anxiety yet remains afraid, remind her that therapeutic exposures, unlike naturally occurring ones, are planned, more frequent, last longer to promote victory, and include avoiding escape (Antony & Swinson, 2000). Grasping this, the client is ready to begin the exposures.

Exposure Therapy in Action

With the client aware of how ET works and motivated to take the next step, it is time to move to developing a plan of exposure and implementing it. In this section, we will discuss the creation of an anxiety hierarchy, issues to be addressed in planning, and the actual implementation of ET.

Building a Hierarchy of Anxiety

People who have anxieties often have more than one fear, and have gradations in the fears they have. Therefore, it is important to do a thorough assessment of these prior to initiating ET. Work with the client to develop a complete list of the things that make him feel anxiety. Then rate them from mildest to most severe. Remember to include mental fears or worries as well. More significant anxieties can be broken down into more and less threatening aspects.

Instruct the person with anxiety how to use a subjective units of distress scale (SUDS) where 1 is a state of near-perfect calm and 100 a state of utter panic. Practice rating different fears (even realistic ones) so the person learns to use such a scale accurately, especially as some people tend toward putting most things higher up the scale. Once the client has learned to use the SUDS, have her use it to rate the different levels of anxiety about a certain topic. Ask her questions to include situational, cognitive, and physiological elements (Abramowitz et al., 2011), as these will lead to situational, imaginal, or interoceptive exposure strategies, respectively. After she has given numerical values to each level of anxiety, rank them from lowest to highest. This yields the foundation of a hierarchy like the one for ants mentioned earlier. For your convenience, you can use the Anxiety Hierarchy form (Form 4.1) at the end of this chapter. Remember, you may need to complete more than one hierarchy per client when multiple anxieties are evident.

Consider a possible hierarchy for a person afraid of dogs. The greatest fear might be actually petting a dog (SUDS score of 95), but the therapist can guide the client to see that he may have a mild reaction to merely talking about a dog (SUDS=28) and a little more if he sees a picture of a dog (or touches that picture; SUDS=52), hears a dog barking (SUDS=67), stands near a fence behind which is a dog (SUDS=75), or is in a room or yard with a dog (SUDS=85).

Issues in Planning Exposures

With client buy-in and a good hierarchy in place, the therapist now needs to strategize the exposure, considering some critical issues. Despite the evidence in support of ET, there is still some variation in thought as to how best to implement it. Exposure therapy is customized to some extent when used with differing disorders, and we will note distinctive features for each in Part II. For now, we will review some major aspects of ET that bear consideration as therapy begins. These will be organized according to four factors delineated by Rosqvist (2005): frequency, duration, severity, and latency.

FREQUENCY OF EXPOSURES

There has been considerable debate in the field as to whether more intense, massed exposures over a short period of time is superior to exposures spaced out more over time (Barlow, 2002; Barlow, Raffa, & Cohen, 2002; Clark & Beck, 2010). To summarize these summaries: while there is still uncertainty, a good option is to begin with frequent exposures, but then spread them out over time once initial learning has occurred. This appears to promote better long-term maintenance of gains (Barlow, 2002). (Foa's prolonged exposure therapy [Foa et al., 2005] will be examined in Chapter 8.)

Clark and Beck (2010) note the manualized treatment approaches on situational exposure recommend sessions daily five days per week over three to four weeks. This is a demanding schedule; another way to maintain momentum is to assign homework as practice between sessions (Rosqvist, 2005), though more frequent appointments early in the therapy may prove helpful. It appears important for the therapist to walk the client through several exposures to encourage her in the initial stages of learning that escape is not necessary, and to coach her to stay with the anxiety until it resolves. In many private practice situations, the therapist will have to strike the best balance of practicality and intensity given time and financial concerns for such an intensive therapy.

DURATION

How long should each session last? Overall it appears that longer exposure sessions are more productive than shorter ones (Foa & Kozak, 1985). But the salient point is whether it achieves the goal of ET: allowing the exposure to continue until the anxiety begins to resolve. Though several different suggestions are in the literature (Clark & Beck, 2010), a reasonable guide appears to be a 50 to 60 percent decrease on the SUDS scale from the original (or highest) score. For example, if the client reaches a score of 80 when listening to a dog bark, she should stay with the barking until that subsides to at most a 40. This can take from one to two hours initially (Rosqvist, 2005), shortening as the client makes progress. This, of course, means that ET won't typically fit into the typical forty-five to fifty-minute session, though Abramowitz et al. (2011) note that many adequate exposure sessions can fit into the typical clinical hour. The client is also encouraged to avoid escape behaviors during the exposure (if one works from a strictly behavioral view of anxiety), and it may prevent habituation if one terminates the exposure before anxiety declines. If you are more focused on exposure as promoting self-efficacy, Clark and Beck (2010) note that you might allow for "controlled escape" (p. 243), whereby the person can escape once she feels the anxiety is intolerable, provided the therapist leads her back into the anxiety soon. They discourage this, however, and believe that any escape may harm both behavioral and cognitive goals. I suggest that the therapist be sure to start at a place on a hierarchy where success seems likely and move only when success at the next level can be expected.

SEVERITY

The next issue facing the clinician is where to begin: with easy exposures or more challenging ones? Here clinical judgment will have to guide the therapist, though a few guidelines exist. Clark and Beck (2010) note that researchers have found success with intensive, massed exposure to the most difficult items on a hierarchy at the outset. Yet, graduated exposures are more palatable to persons with anxiety. Given that dropout is a concern in ET to begin with, the therapist risks the client dropping out of therapy if the exposures are too hard in the beginning. So, generally it is good to begin exposures with lower items on the hierarchy, moving up the list at a steady pace so that progress will be made toward the more challenging ones.

LATENCY

Latency refers to the delay between the person's being asked to begin the exposure and his actually doing so. Think of diving into a pool. If you climb up onto the diving board and hesitate out of fear, jumping in becomes harder the longer you wait. So it is with exposures: the client needs to do them as soon as instructed; "hesitation reifies the fear" (Rosqvist, 2005, p. 48). Of course, this holds true in day-to-day life as well. If the person with anxiety learns to keep moving toward anxious situations without slowing or pausing, he will be more successful in facing them.

Structuring the Sessions

Once the therapist has thought through these issues, it is time to initiate exposure sessions. The therapist will have to determine whether the sessions need to take place in the office or in the field. If the exposure is to be gradual, the early sessions might take place in the office until the client understands the flow of exposure sessions and builds some confidence. Location will also depend on the type of exposure. Imaginal exposure is generally suited to the office, and there are many resources in and near the typical office to facilitate interoceptive exposure. More variability will be involved in situational exposure.

Abramowitz et al. (2011) suggest the typical session begin with a five- to ten-minute check-in and review of the past session and any homework. Client and counselor agree to an exposure task and it is introduced. After the exposure, about fifteen minutes is devoted to debriefing the experience, assigning any homework, and planning what exposure will occur in the next session (and where it will occur).

Early on, the therapist may wish to review the rationale for the exposure and offer encouragement and support to the client. The therapist may use the Exposure Session Plan (Form 4.2, at the end of this chapter) to set up the events ahead. Note which fear is being addressed, and where on the hierarchy the exposure will occur. After the first session, the therapist might review the previous session and progress to date. Recall with the client what the feared outcome is and that it is highly unlikely (though generally not impossible). Take care not to engage in reassurance (allowing for a safety behavior), but reorient the client's questions to the fact that together you will test them experientially. Review likely safety behaviors associated with this anxiety, and commit together to preventing them.

It is generally preferred that the client not engage in any form of distraction (for example, thinking she is somewhere else, intentionally thinking about something pleasant, or even thinking of something in the environment other than the feared situation), as these hamper the emotional processing that exposure is intended to promote (Foa & Kozak, 1986). Rather, encourage the client to pay close attention to her anxiety and the elements of it while not trying to fight or suppress it (Clark & Beck, 2010).

Take a baseline SUDS reading and record it. Invite the client into the exposure, and praise his success if he promptly engages in it. Encourage him if he is hesitant. Take another SUDS reading about every five minutes as the exposure progresses, asking the client to rate his current feelings. Stay positive in your interactions, and terminate the exercise when the SUDS reaches 50 percent of its highest value. The Exposure Session Plan includes a graph that can now be completed to visually assist the client in understanding his experience. Discuss the experience and the graph and how it matched or did not match the client's expectations. Jointly make a plan for homework to continue the exposures (Abramowitz et al. [2011] recommend at least one to two hours of practice with exposure daily) and the plan for the next exposure therapy session.

Continue sessions in a similar fashion, increasing the difficulty regularly until the client is facing the items highest on her hierarchy. If there are several hierarchies, proceed to the next once the first is accomplished. Each subsequent target should go more quickly and easily as *generalization* (moving learning from one situation to broader contexts) does its job.

Exposure therapy is not easy, so continue to review the importance of the exposures, the rationale behind them, and the problems with escape and avoidance. Maintain an encouraging tone while holding firm to the goals. This is difficult for many counselors who enjoy offering acceptance and affirmation to clients. Certainly affirmation of the effort required to do ET is in order, but often a caring tone of gentle challenge is in order to scaffold the client to complete exposures.

Once the most troubling items on the hierarchies are conquered, spacing out sessions and having occasional follow-up can help maintain gains and prevent slipping back into previous patterns. Also, monitor for any symptom substitution, as occasionally another anxiety or obsession will arise to replace ones that have been mastered.

Overcoming Logistic and Ethical Issues in ET

In Chapter 1 we noted that there are a number of hurdles to ET that can discourage therapists from utilizing it. Exposure therapy does not fit neatly into typical therapy time slots and may require the therapist to get out of his office. Moreover, ET has some poor press and is criticized for being harsh and for provoking anxiety (Richard & Gloster, 2007). In concluding this chapter, we will take a brief look at why these concerns are not sufficient to warrant staying away from ET.

The Practicality of ET

Many exposures take more time than the typical session permits. Moreover, insurance companies do not often accommodate this, despite the strong empirical support for it. Also, ET works best if the early sessions at least are fairly frequent, something again frowned on by most third-party payers. This is a call to mental health professionals to educate insurance companies and other third parties that not all evidence-based treatments fit into a once-per-week fifty-minute session. In fact, because ET is efficacious, it may cost much less money in the long run than less effective treatments done in traditional sessions. Therapists also do well to learn more about what *is* covered and whether less familiar current procedural terminology (CPT) codes might be available to cover ET.

Therapists may also explain to their clients that even if some of the treatment must be paid out of pocket, the overall expense of therapy could be less than if less effective treatments are used that take more time—and thus more money. Many clients may be willing to pay more to get better faster, *if* they understand the rationale and benefits.

Exposure therapy may require some flexibility of scheduling. Most sessions will fit nicely if two consecutive appointment times are allotted for the ET session. This can allow for a short trip during the session if needed. If a larger portion of a particular practice is dedicated to ET, then flexible scheduling on a couple of days per week can also accommodate the customized time frames of the exposures.

The changing times also raise the possibility of differing delivery systems. Barlow et al. (2002) reviewed literature to find studies offering some evidence that computer- and book-instructed exposure were equally effective (Ghosh & Marks, 1987). Telephone administration of self-exposure instructions also found support in the work of Swinson, Fergus, Cox, and Wickwire (1995). Cell phones and video calls afford opportunities to adapt the principles of ET so that the therapist is present without being in the same room. Personal digital devices open up the possibility of applications that might assist exposure. Research on these will be needed, and the ethical issues well thought out prior to implementation, but as health care delivery changes in many ways, mental health care likely will be moving away from its overdependence on fifty-minute sessions, and ET may fit well with these changes.

The Ethics of ET

Observing that while patients generally are accepting of ET as they experience its benefits, Prochaska and Norcross (1999) voice concern that it is *therapists* who express concerns with its appropriateness. Many of us are trained to be warm and tolerant in the context of talk therapy and are not acculturated into the structure and direction, much less the intense emotions, involved in ET. Pushing already troubled individuals to fully experience discomfort—on purpose—is contrary to much therapeutic training and may lead to suspicion that it is somehow unethical. Richard and Gloster (2007) surveyed clinicians and litigation records to see if there is truth to this idea. They found no legal proceedings due to use of ET, and, when they surveyed clinicians on the subject, they concluded that "exposure therapy appears to be relatively free of ethical and legal complaints even though it may be viewed as aversive by professionals and may not be the treatment of choice by outpatients and students" (p. 424). The key to accepting ET is that therapists get appropriate training and that they communicate the rationale clearly to their clients. The great majority of clinicians are well enough trained to know what is pushing too far when asking clients to deliberately enter into strong emotions. If ET is as effective as the research suggests, *not* using it when it is indicated may come closer to being an ethical issue.

None of this is to discourage therapists from due diligence when doing ET. Certainly clients should not be pushed beyond the limits of what they can tolerate. Moreover, common clinical sense is warranted when therapy moves out of the office. Counselors should not be alone in clients' homes, nor drive with clients in their cars, without appropriate insurance. In most traditional exposure approaches, the therapist is with the client as he faces feared things such as shopping malls or driving. The key is to keep in role as therapist and not enter dual relationships such as chauffeur, visitor, and so on. Cueing a client to use breathing and mindfulness as he stands on a bridge is not an ethical issue so long as the visit to the bridge is focused on the exposure and is built into the treatment plan; it is when outings move beyond therapy that problems may arise. Most therapists are trained adequately enough regarding boundaries to avoid this so long as they don't forget the other aspects of the therapeutic relationship while endeavoring to accomplish exposures.

Confidentiality needs to be protected when doing exposures in public, something that should be discussed with the client beforehand, and consent obtained. Try to plan exposures in places where the client is less likely to encounter people she knows, and work out a plan for what to say if an acquaintance approaches her. The client should be the one to speak, should be free to say what has been planned, and should have the option of introducing the counselor or not. If it is agreed the client would not want to be "exposed" as being on a counseling-related outing, then the counselor should help the client plan on some neutral way to explain who the counselor is to the friend. For example, she might say that the counselor is a friend she has met with to discuss some private matters. The key is to be thoughtful and plan ahead to avoid potential ethical pitfalls.

Types of Exposure

To conclude our review of the basics of conducting therapeutic exposure, we will survey the major types of exposures that can be incorporated into treatment—imaginal, interoceptive, virtual reality, and situational, or in vivo.

Imaginal Exposure

One basic rule in exposure is that the more realistic the exposure, the better. Thus, we will see that when possible, in vivo, or situational, exposures are best because they occur in the real-world setting of the thing one fears. Yet, imaginal exposures are very common and are useful in at least two sorts of situations. First, imagining the feared scenario may be a starting place for clients who are not ready to face their fears in the real world just yet. So, imaginal exposures are often items lower on an exposure hierarchy. The second occasion for imaginal exposure is if the target itself is a mental phenomenon. Abramowitz et al. (2011) note that three types of feared items may actually occur in the mind, being mental images of some kind. Two of these types are most commonly associated with OCD—obsessions and unwanted impulses. Obsessions often take the form of thoughts that intrude into one's consciousness and are unwanted; for example, blasphemous thoughts for persons with religious obsessions. The other frequent mental image associated with OCD is the unwanted impulse to act improperly. Abramowitz et al.'s third type is traumatic memories, which are generally associated with PTSD. As these all occur in the mind, the exposure must take place there. The client is asked to think the thought or image and avoid mental escape or avoidance, often while bearing in mind that these thoughts are just thoughts and not true desires.

Working with these cognitive phenomena that evoke anxiety is the first of the three types of imaginal exposures delineated by Abramowitz et al. (2011). This first type is the direct confrontation of these troublesome thoughts and/or memories and is called *primary* imaginal exposure. *Secondary* imaginal exposure is used when a person has fears of disastrous outcomes that may ensue from certain situations. Imaginal exposure is then a supplement to in vivo exposure to enable the client to be exposed to the disastrous outcomes she (unnecessarily) fears and that will not occur in the real world. The third type is *preliminary* imaginal exposure; these are simply those imaginal exposures used to teach the basic skills of handling an exposure and to prepare the individual for in vivo exposures to come. These are often helpful starting places, but may not be effective for those who struggle to create images with enough detail to evoke a fear response (Rosqvist, 2005). They are vital in some models of exposure therapy—such as narrative exposure therapy (Schauer, Neuner, & Elbert, 2005) and prolonged exposure therapy (Foa, Hembree, & Rothbaum, 2007)—that we will cover in Chapter 8.

One important variant of imaginal exposure is written exposure (Hoodin & Gillis, 2007). Writing as a therapeutic intervention has been espoused by Pennebaker (1997). Rather than simply visualize an unpleasant situation or fear mentally, one can write it down in detail. Clients can do this on their own and bring their work to a subsequent session. This simply adds a way to promote organization and, when the feared item is an event, a narrative that can be helpful. Similar to writing is recording a client detailing a traumatic event or feared situation. This might be done in session and the client encouraged to review it for exposure practice between sessions.

Regardless of the particular approach to imaginal exposure, it is vital that the target of the exposure be imagined vividly and with emotion (Rosqvist, 2005). The therapist interacts with the client in session by asking questions to evoke greater detail of the event and physical and emotional sensations associated with it. For example, if a person who is afraid of flying is imagining walking onto an airplane, it would be important to elicit the sights of the jetway, the sounds of people coming and going and of the engines, the change in air temperature as one walks, and the smell of jet fuel in the air. The person would also be encouraged to identify physical sensations such as muscle tension, light-headedness, and increased heart rate.

Props and media can also be mustered to support imaginal exposure. While these may involve external stimuli, they are not the actual feared object or situation, so the exposure is still imaginal. A person who is afraid of injections might read a pamphlet about how to give injections or view a picture or video of a hypodermic needle. These may enhance purely mental exposures by evoking a greater fear response. Thus for many people they may fall a bit higher on the hierarchy than visualized representations and may serve as a step toward in vivo exposure.

Interoceptive Exposure

Some persons who are highly anxious also become fearful of the actual physical symptoms of anxiety itself, which only exacerbates the symptoms. A feedback loop is created wherein the person's fear increases, which in turn causes the physiological symptoms to escalate. This is a core characteristic of panic disorder as this feedback loop is the recipe for a panic attack. In such cases, the person may come to fear the sensations themselves more than an object, thought, or situation; the sensations may include dizziness, upset stomach, increased heart rate, and tightness in the chest (Rosqvist, 2005).

Forsyth, Fusé, and Acheson (2008) present a detailed model for conducting interoceptive exposures that will serve as our guide. First, it is important to place these exposures into the overall treatment plan and address them only after panic attacks have been monitored enough to determine associated symptoms and behaviors. Behavioral experiments (such as having the client do things or go places to determine which are more likely to evoke anxiety) may also help identify items for the hierarchy. As with any exposure, the client should be provided with a satisfactory rationale for this therapy, and then a hierarchy can be constructed. (I would add that interoceptive exposures may be the best place to start in panic disorders, but may be a separate exposure hierarchy in other forms of anxiety disorders when physical symptoms are prominent.)

Forsyth et al. (2008) suggest beginning with in-session exposures that then move to at-home practice between sessions, beginning with easier tasks before moving to ones that are more anxiety-evoking. They stress the need for interoceptive exposures to be done in a variety of settings that might be associated with the symptoms so as to promote generalization. The therapist monitors for signs of avoidance or escape behaviors and works to prevent these responses. This monitoring becomes more the client's responsibility as exposures move out of the office, though a trusted friend might go with the client as she does interoceptive exposures in public places. Having someone go along with the client can enhance compliance and help monitor escape and avoidance. Chapter 12 offers some ideas for ways to simulate anxious sensations so as to promote interoceptive exposure.

Virtual Reality Exposure

A fascinating and very promising approach to exposure is virtual reality (VR). Given that the approach generally follows a graded hierarchy of exposures, it is sometimes called "VR-graded exposure" (Wiederhold, Gervitz, & Spira, 2001). While pictures and videos can be somewhat helpful, they are not nearly as powerful as the exposure possible using ever-improving virtual reality technologies (Rosqvist, 2005); this can particularly help individuals who are less adept at using mental imagery. Bouchard, Côté, and Richard (2007) offer a helpful summary of this approach to exposure and note that not only is VR more powerful than imaginal exposure, but it is often a safer option than in vivo exposure.

In contrast to merely viewing a video of a feared situation, VR technology (Bouchard et al., 2007) immerses the person in a situation that is viewed three-dimensionally, that is interactive, and from which she cannot walk away. Programs permit quite realistic exposures to situations through the senses, creating sensations very closely approximating reality. The authors note that no studies have yet shown that VR exposures do not work, and VR has thus generated eager research interest and a substantial literature on its use.

The negative side of VR exposure is the expense of the equipment (Bouchard et al., 2007), which can range from a head-mounted display with headphones for audio to more elaborate, room-sized settings costing over $250,000. Due to the expense, VR exposure is not likely an option for most readers of this book. Nonetheless, a recent meta-analysis (Powers & Emmelkamp, 2008) makes clear that it is a very effective method of treatment for anxiety disorders, with there even being some data suggesting it is more effective than in vivo exposures. Bouchard et al. (2007) illustrate that it is helpful for fear of flying, spider phobia, fear of public speaking/social anxiety, fear of heights, PTSD, driving phobia, panic disorder with agoraphobia, and claustrophobia.

There are no virtual reality exposure options in Part II; I refer those interested in knowing more to the Bouchard et al. (2007) and Powers and Emmelkamp (2008) articles.

In Vivo Exposure

Live (or in vivo/in situ) exposure has been the gold standard of behavior therapies for anxiety for several decades (Hazlett-Stevens & Craske, 2008) and has proven effective across the spectrum of anxiety disorders. While one might start here with some fears, in vivo exposure is more often administered after the client has moved up from less threatening imaginal exposures. This preparatory imaginal work has the added benefit of the individual's learning how to manage exposures so he is better able to cope with in vivo experiences, which largely occur outside the clinician's office.

The protocol was covered earlier in the chapter, but several reminders may be in order here. It is important that the client choose to enter into the exposure, to prevent its being ineffective or even potentially worsening the anxiety (Rosqvist, 2005). The therapist should take care not to push the exposure onto the client so much that the client does it while feeling pressured and thus does not truly choose to do it. It is also often helpful for the therapist to model how to think and act during an exposure and even to predict how the client might feel. Once the exposure begins, it is of course important that the client not distract herself from the situation or use other escape strategies, but rather remain in the anxious setting until her anxiety subsides to a moderate degree. Exposures done between sessions without the therapist present should be reviewed at the next session and victories celebrated, while therapist and client troubleshoot and fine-tune the approach so as to continue progress into the next round of exposures. Finally, the individual will work his way up the hierarchy as he manages less anxiety-evoking items with considerable success.

We have now seen the basics of how exposure is implemented and the types that might be called upon in planning treatment. Exposure is a very flexible technique and is easily incorporated into a variety of therapeutic models. In the chapters that follow, we will look at some of the major ways this can be done.

Form 4.1 Anxiety Hierarchy

Thing Causing Anxiety: ____________________

Think through as many situations as you can for this topic and rate how facing each of these situations makes you feel on a SUDS scale of 1 (not anxious at all) to 100 (as anxious as it's possible to feel). Rank-order them from highest (most anxiety evoking) to lowest (least anxiety evoking). On a fresh copy of this form, rewrite the list in rank order, with the SUDS number, so that you have an ordered hierarchy from highest to lowest.

Example: A person who fears public speaking might have a hierarchy that begins with just thinking about speaking to a group (SUDS = 15) and moves up to watching a video of someone giving a speech and imagining doing it himself (32), to talking to a friend in public (43) to ordering at a fast-food restaurant (63) to talking at a dinner with some people he just met (75) to speaking in a class at school (88) to being on television (98).

Situation	SUDS (1–100)	Ranking

Form 4.2 Exposure Session Plan

Date: ___________ Location: ____

Primary Fear: ____

SUDS Rating on Hierarchy of Today's Exposure: ___________

Exposure Plan:

Exposure Target:

How to be accomplished:

What I fear might happen:

Safety Behaviors to Avoid:

SUDS Ratings:

0 min ______ 5 min ______ 10 min ______ 15 min ______ 20 min ______ 25 min ______

30 min ______ 35 min ______ 40 min ______ 45 min ______ 50 min ______ 55 min ______

60 min ______ 65 min ______ 70 min ______ 75 min ______ 80 min ______ 85 min ______

90 min ______

Graph of SUDS Ratings

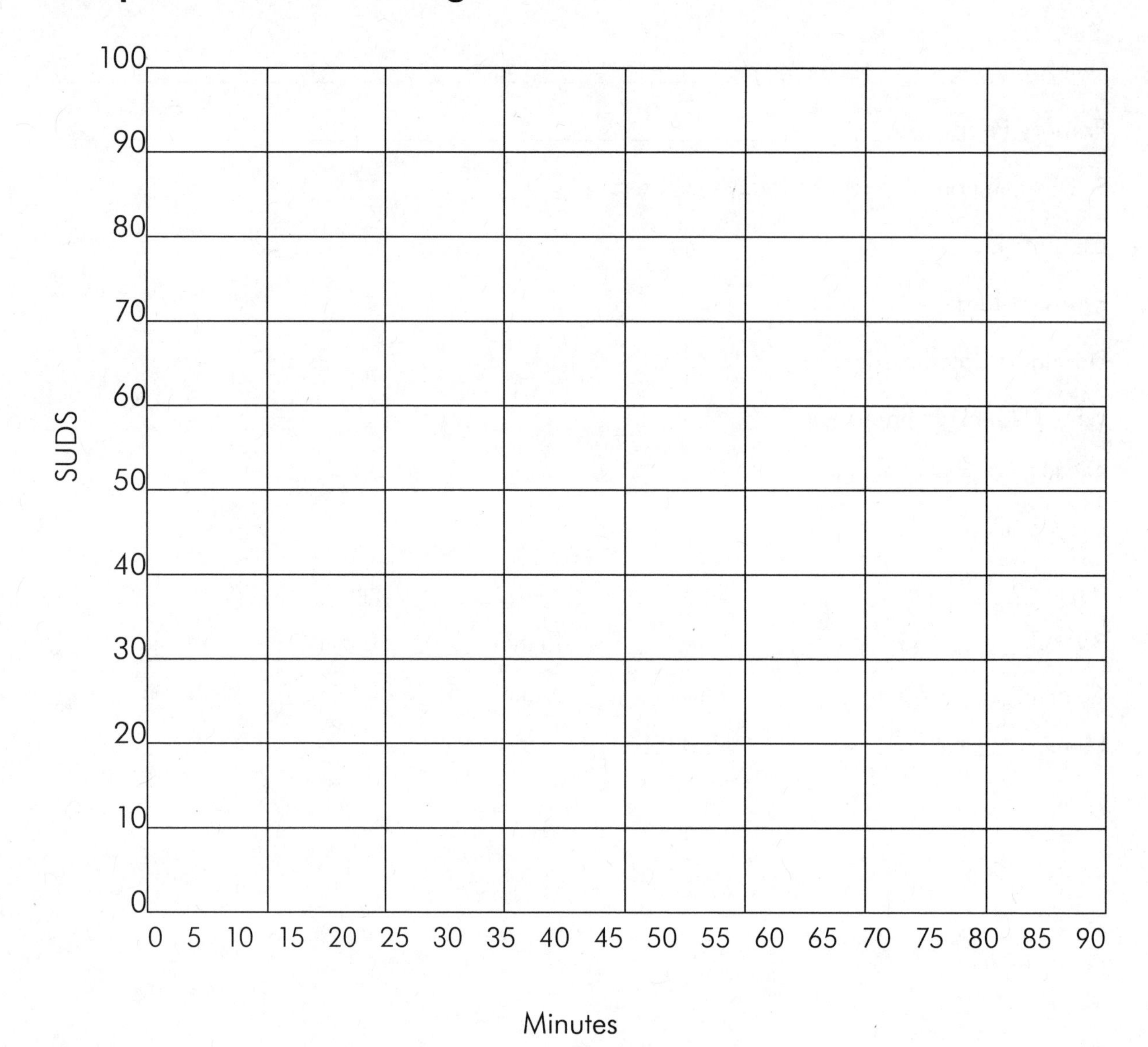

Comments:

CHAPTER 5

Exposure Therapy and Response Prevention in the Context of Cognitive Behavioral Therapy

A major theme of our discussion of exposure therapy (ET) and response prevention (RP) has been that they are techniques rather than therapies unto themselves. They are at their foundation behavioral techniques with roots in animal learning models (see Chapter 2). As such, they depend on the notion that merely being exposed to a fear stimulus until anxiety subsides can overwrite the association in memory and resolve the emotion. This strictly behavioral version of ET can work on its own, particularly in simple phobias.

But humans are thinking creatures, and the "black box" of cognition that early behaviorists avoided (since thinking is not clearly observable and measurable, as empiricism supposedly required) is now studied widely. Cognition has its own branch of psychology, and cognitive processes are widely believed to play a major role in our emotional functioning (Clark & Beck, 2010). This belief undergirds the growth of a major force in psychotherapy, cognitive behavioral therapy (CBT). Built on the premise that thinking impacts feelings and behavior, CBT opens the broad spectrum of cognitive processes up to therapeutic use. Behavioral techniques such as ET and RP have a role in this more comprehensive approach; this chapter is a guide to the basics of using CBT for anxiety and how exposure and response prevention are contextualized into it. This will be the first of four chapters in which we explore how the basic processes of ET and RP can be adapted into broader models of therapy to enhance our effectiveness in treating anxiety.

Cognitive behavioral therapy maintains behaviorism's commitment to empirical research and thus has been a pioneer in demonstrating that it is an evidence-based treatment. Dobson and Dobson (2009) list major review articles that show CBT to be effective for anxiety disorders, specifically listing references for specific phobias, social anxiety disorder, obsessive-compulsive disorder, panic disorder, post-traumatic stress disorder, and generalized anxiety disorder. Indeed, Fisher and O'Donohue (2006) show that CBT is effective for over seventy mental disturbances, including the anxiety disorders.

Cognitive behavioral therapy is a family of treatments sharing the common assumptions that cognition affects behavior, cognition can be tracked and changed, and desired change in behavior can be affected through cognitive change (Dobson & Dozois, 2001). This "mediational" model argues, and has empirically demonstrated, that cognitive processes indeed mediate between stimulus input and behavioral output. Dobson and Dozois (2001) trace the movement of basic cognitive science into therapies that blend the cognitive and behavioral dimensions. Major models have included Ellis's rational emotive behavioral therapy, which is built largely on the notion of irrational beliefs underlying psychopathology. Meichenbaum's contribution in self-instructional training focuses on treating mediational problems through clearer problem-solving skills and coping statements.

Other important schools emerged, but maybe the most significant one is Beck's cognitive therapy, which focuses on the misappraisal of events as central to psychological difficulty. Beck was joined by Clark (2010) in developing a comprehensive cognitive model for anxiety that incorporates behavioral elements, and their vital work will guide our discussion of CBT for anxiety and the roles of ET and RP in it.

Clark and Beck's Cognitive Model of Anxiety

Clark and Beck (2010) do not deny that learning theory is important in understanding anxiety, but they present evidence to show that the strength and persistence of fear conditioning is largely a function of cognitive appraisal. They distinguish fear, the basic cognitive process at work when threatening stimuli are present, from anxiety, the ongoing state perpetuated by exaggerated threat appraisals. These faulty thought processes are the target for cognitive therapy. (Note that Clark and Beck call their model "cognitive therapy" but incorporate behavioral treatments in it. Thus, it does exemplify a CBT approach, but we will use their term in our discussion.)

For Clark and Beck (2010), the cognitive perspective on anxiety is focused on the concept of *vulnerability*, the perception of feeling subject to dangers within or without while lacking enough control over the situation to provide a sense of safety. The two pivotal issues around which anxiety revolves are the *primary appraisal* of threat, which includes a propensity to miss signs of safety in the environment, and *secondary processing*, which elaborates on this initial appraisal, particularly in terms of one's estimation of one's ability to cope with the feared stimulus and find safety from it. The hypotheses undergirding this model have largely been supported by empirical data (though several merit additional research attention).

Overview of the Cognitive Model

These foundational tenets are organized into the model presented in Figure 5.1 (Clark & Beck, 2010). The anxiety sequence begins when a situation, event, or other stimulus triggers an appraisal of threat. This is a *diathesis-stress model*, where there is a predisposition (diathesis) that makes one more likely to experience anxiety when encountering a trigger (stress). Many persons who experience undue anxiety have a diathesis whereby they more readily generate appraisals of danger anyway, this cognitive bias being built in through experience and/or a history of cognitions that make them vulnerable to perceiving threats more than need be. The particular fears that trigger the anxiety response will vary from person to person and be largely determined by the individual's strivings in the areas of achieving and maintaining social relationships that affirm the self, or in threatening one's sense of personal mastery and independence. For example, a person whose cognitions overvalue the need for approval might trigger anxiety when she appraises that a peer has shunned her in a social setting. Or, the thought that there might be germs on a doorknob may trigger anxiety in the person who overestimates the likelihood that germs will cause him serious illness and thus threaten his independence and well-being. Cognitive therapy will work to identify and alter these distorted beliefs that lead to overestimates of what is threatening.

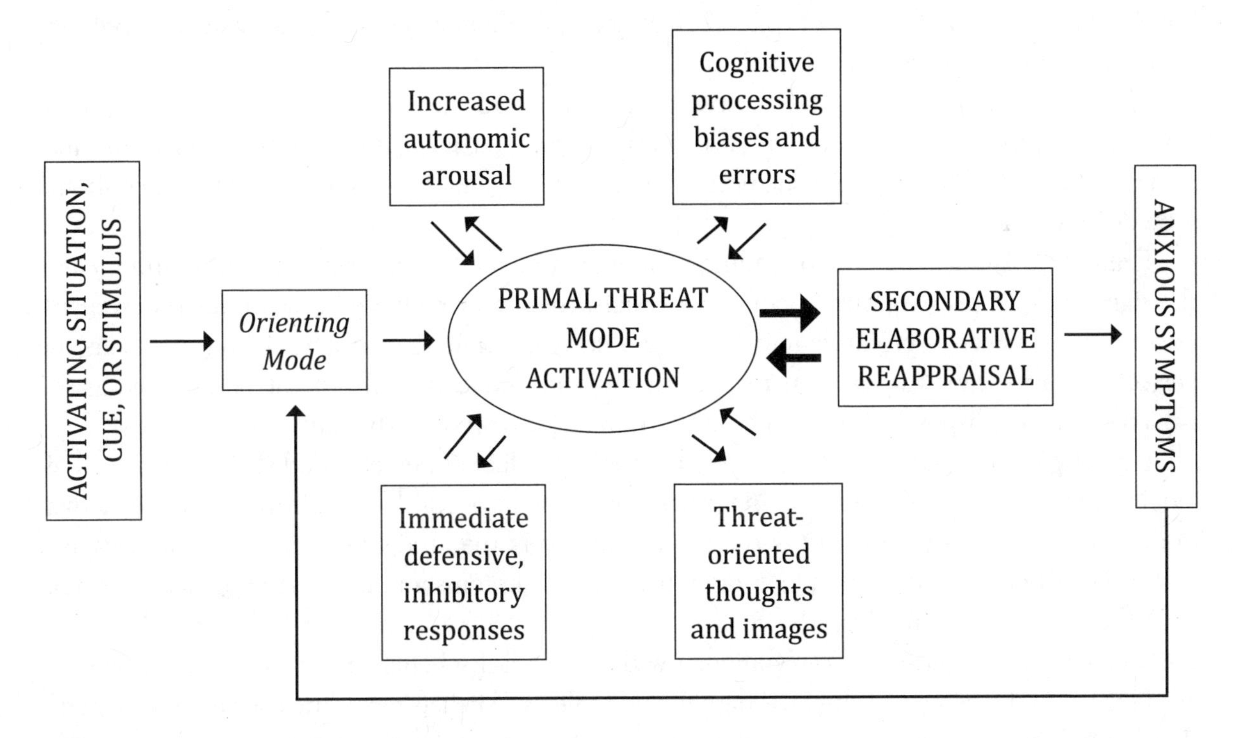

Figure 5.1 Cognitive Model of Anxiety

From *Cognitive Therapy of Anxiety Disorders* (p. 32), by D. A. Clark and A. T. Beck, 2010, New York: The Guilford Press. Adapted with permission.

ORIENTING MODE

A cluster of *schemas* (cognitive constructions) are activated to provide an initial perception of a stimulus and are triggered if the schemas activated match an orienting template for threat. This *orienting mode* is rather broad and will sense only a raw notion of negative and personally relevant stimuli. This notion is more of a perception than a conceptually driven appraisal. In anxiety, the orienting mode is oriented toward attending to and perceiving negative emotional material (a preconscious attentional bias) that will shortly be interpreted as a threat. For instance, a veteran with PTSD might react viscerally to the sound of a balloon popping at his child's birthday party. This heightened alertness to threat will be a challenge to overcoming anxiety.

PRIMAL THREAT MODE

The detection of negative emotional information will simultaneously activate the *primal threat mode*, which is dubbed "primal" as it is a set of schemas concerned with maximizing safety and minimizing danger for the organism. Once these threat schemas are activated they dominate cognitive activities and make it a challenge for the anxious person to process anything other than the perceived threat. In the case of our veteran, he might stop cutting the cake and start scanning for potential dangers. In Clark and Beck's (2010) model, five major types of schemas come into play in the activation of primal threat mode.

Cognitive-conceptual schemas are those that incorporate the individual's beliefs and assumptions relevant to determining risk, building on the storage, retrieval, and interpretation of information about threat. These also include notions of how vulnerable the person may be to threat should it be detected (and thus influence safety behaviors).

Behavioral schemas are action readiness plans that enable quick defensive action and include the fight-or-flight response. In anxious individuals, these may be biased toward quick movement toward safety, which is promptly reinforced by a decrease in anxiety. Such schemas may bias the person toward escape rather than reappraising the objective risk the threat poses, leaving the person with a predisposition to escape rather than address anxious thoughts.

Physiological schemas are those that enable the individual to perceive and then evaluate physiological arousal (autonomic arousal and other physical sensations) that results from anxiety activation. These may be key in panic as the person interprets the anxiety symptoms themselves as a threat to well-being, leading to a looping of increased symptoms and increased appraisal of threat from the symptoms themselves.

Motivational schemas are closely aligned with behavioral schemas in forming one's intentions with regard to the perceived threat. These include rules and beliefs regarding the value of escaping the threat. They also react to a perception of a loss of control when threatened as an outcome that must be avoided.

Affective schemas perceive feeling states and respond to the subjective experience of emotion. They are particularly focused on survival and on channeling attention to the perceived threat.

Activating these schemas when anxious can lead to increases in feelings of nervousness or agitation, or feeling "on edge" (Clark & Beck, 2010, p. 46).

Cognitive and behavioral interventions are used to decrease the ready accessibility and power of these schemas, which play such a major role in the experience of anxiety.

The actions in the cognitive model of anxiety thus far are all fairly automatic. In most persons, these various schemas are fairly adept at discerning genuine threat and proper reaction, but of course that is not the case for those with anxiety disorders. Whether activated appropriately or not, once primal threat mode springs into action, four processes respond to it and in turn influence it. These processes can then exacerbate the sense of anxiety and the urgency of escape (conflicting with the requirement in ET that the person be exposed to the threat cue).

Threat mode will take autonomic arousal "at its word" and assume that the actual danger is as dangerous as the strong feelings suggest. Such powerful physical sensations are hard to resist, and they strongly compel the individual to take action to reduce them (making exposures and response prevention more difficult). A second process spurred by the activation of threat mode is *defensive inhibitory processes,* which are almost reflexive in response to the threat appraisal. So it is that persons with OCD may grab for the hand sanitizer or those with social anxiety may avoid eye contact with little conscious planning to do so. Third, in response to threat mode activation, *cognitive processing errors* are likely, as processes are more selective toward the threat and biased against safety cues. Here is where many cognitive therapy techniques are mustered to fight tendencies to distort and misjudge situations. Finally, *automatic threat-relevant thoughts and danger images* may be the consequence of threat mode activation. These may be involuntary and intrude into one's thinking. The veteran mentioned above, for instance, might suddenly recall images of being in battle when he hears the balloon pop. Cognitive therapists teach clients strategies to reduce the adverse consequences of these mechanisms.

All we have covered thus far happens fairly quickly in real time and is followed by *secondary elaboration and reappraisal,* the next module in the cognitive model of anxiety.

SECONDARY ELABORATION AND REAPPRAISAL

A history of learned fears and core cognitive beliefs and schemas "program" the triggering and processing of primal threat mode. But once activated, the mind proceeds to process and appraise the situation, with this secondary reappraisal following inevitably upon the activation of the primal threat mode. Secondary processing is more conscious and controlled, according to Clark and Beck (2010), and it feeds back into the primal threat mode, for better or worse. If this elaboration process cannot produce a plausible alternative to the initial appraisal of threat, the anxiety may worsen. This is commonly the case for those with excessive anxiety. Five phenomena play a role in this secondary cognitive analysis of the threat.

First, the person appraises his or her *ability to cope with the perceived threat.* One may demonstrate what Clark and Beck (2010, p. 48) refer to as "self-confidence" and determine that one has assets to master problems and can use them to do so. If not, that individual will feel vulnerable to the perceived threat. The outcome of this appraisal may rest on whether the person even has the skills to cope. One is particularly vulnerable if one lacks the skills and the ability to put them to use. An appraisal of such incompetence makes the individual tentative and motivates a retreat (escape behavior) when anxiety is experienced. If the person actually has coping skills, cognitive therapy will correct the maladaptive evaluation; if skills are lacking, they will be taught.

A second elaborative process is the *search for safety cues*. If the person overlooks these, or has a restricted view of what is safe, she may use inappropriate safety-seeking strategies. The anxious individual may be biased toward seeking short-term cues to provide immediate relief from anxiety. For example, a person afraid of getting stuck in an elevator may not notice the buttons that can be used for emergencies, but rather completely avoid getting in an elevator. Cognitive therapy addresses the dysfunctional appraisal of the danger and works to eliminate inappropriate safety-seeking behaviors (this, as we will soon see, is where ET and RP come in).

Many persons with excessive anxiety almost reflexively move toward self-protection and escape. However, more realistic coping resources might be accessed, and these schemas are called *constructive mode thinking*. Aspects of this mode include reflective thought, problem solving, and a reassessing of the purportedly threatening situation, all leading to more constructive, adaptive responses to the situation. Cognitive therapy encourages clients to develop and utilize the constructive thinking mode.

A fourth phenomenon in secondary elaboration is the *initiation of worry*. Once the primal threat mode is activated, worry is a potential by-product. This is a productive activity if it is applied to active problem-solving, but for those with anxiety, it can become a self-perpetuating elaboration of the initial threat and confirm that threat as being more threatening than it actually is. This process is particularly evident in those with generalized anxiety disorder, and it follows that cognitive therapy would address the worrying in order to reduce it.

Finally, the outcome of this entire secondary appraisal process is a more *conscious process of evaluating the perceived threat*. When anxiety is low, this can result in a reduction of anxiety through more realistic valuing of the situation, or through use of good problem-solving techniques to resolve it. In contrast, persons in more anxious states will be biased toward using this reappraisal to confirm their initial appraisal of the stimulus as threatening. Therapy is aimed at helping clients process disconfirming evidence to lower the appraisal of the threat.

This model forms a structure for conceptualizing and planning treatment, and Appendix 5.11 in Clark and Beck (2010, pp. 176–178) provides a very helpful form to develop a case conceptualization based on the cognitive model summarized here.

Goals and Interventions Based on the Cognitive Model

The cognitive model of Clark and Beck (2010) offers a detailed understanding of how CBT views anxiety and readily leads into a set of goals for therapy and techniques for pursuing them. It is to these that we now turn our attention.

Goals of Cognitive Therapy for Anxiety

Recall that Clark and Beck (2010) call their model simply "cognitive," though they incorporate behavioral interventions and thus make it an exemplar of CBT for anxiety, including a place for exposure therapy and response prevention in it. In introducing their interventions, they posit five major goals for cognitive therapists as they work with anxious clients. These follow, adapted into statement form.

1. *Shift the client's focus away from the "threat" and guide her into understanding that appraisals and beliefs are the cause of anxiety.* This goal is to be achieved *not* by logic and persuasion on the part of the counselor, but by cognitive restructuring and empirical hypothesis-testing, which are described a little later in this chapter.
2. *Modify biased threats, safety appraisals, and beliefs.* The therapist is to look for faulty probability estimates ("I am sure I will start shaking during the interview"), faulty severity estimates ("If I do, she will laugh and run me out of her office"), faulty vulnerability estimates ("I will completely fall apart if I start to shake"), and faulty safety estimates ("I'm sure she will be paying a lot of attention to how nervous I am and base her impression on that alone").
3. *Normalize fear and anxiety to reduce absorption in one's symptoms.* The therapist will help the client do this in relation, first, to others by showing that they, too, experience symptoms of anxiety. Second, they are normalized with respect to past experiences, as many anxious people can recall times when the feared stimulus was not nearly as fearful. Finally, symptoms are normalized in relation to situations by showing other situations that might trigger thoughts and symptoms without evoking anxiety. For example, shorter breath after a vigorous workout does not signal danger but is a normal response to exercise. The central concept in all of this is that threat is ubiquitous for everyone.
4. *Strengthen personal efficacy.* The cognitive model observes that beliefs and sometimes history can leave a person feeling low in self-confidence. Cognitive therapy corrects such misperceptions by providing training in coping skills and illuminating the discrepancy

between a person's predicted and actual ability to cope. Often this is accomplished through encouraging experiences in which the client can build self-confidence.

5. *Develop adaptive approaches to safety.* The cognitive model states that anxiety is exacerbated and perpetuated by maladaptive safety beliefs and actions. Therapy, then, will address faulty assumptions about how risky some things are (for example, by noting how some others face them without undue anxiety). Homework assignments can supplement the therapeutic work of learning to attend to safety cues that are often missed (for example, noting that the coffee pot has an automatic timer to turn it off so that even if the client left it on, it will turn itself off). Finally, therapy will identify and correct dysfunctional avoidance and safety seeking (here is where response prevention will play a role).

Cognitive Interventions

The goals just described are achieved through cognitive and behavioral interventions applied at appropriate points in Clark and Beck's (2010) cognitive model. Three major cognitive interventions are utilized, with several ancillary ones also having a place in treatment.

Education of the client is a fundamental intervention strategy in cognitive therapy, beginning with an explanation of the nature of cognitive (and behavioral) therapy. Clark and Beck note that failure to provide an adequate orientation to the nature of treatment is a primary reason for dropout. This is particularly important for something as challenging as exposure therapy.

Orientation to cognitive therapy is only the beginning of education as a vital technique. Figure 5.2 offers a client-friendly version of Clark and Beck's model that can aid in the educational process. For those with anxiety disorders, a solid understanding of anxiety and the role of fear is crucial, with fear being seen as a perceived threat to one's safety or security and anxiety a more complex and persistent feeling of unease or apprehension surrounding a perception of threat to one's interests. An explanation of the normal adaptive value of fear is important given the irrational understandings likely to be evident in the client. The client is instructed in the cognitive model of anxiety and in how anxiety can be inappropriately activated, with the consequences of this inappropriate activation being explained as well. The therapist coaches the client on the nature of escape and avoidance as efforts to avoid anxiety and how these can accidentally worsen anxiety. Finally, clients can see the treatment's major goal of turning off the anxiety program from unnecessary activation and how interventions will move him toward it. It is important also to educate the client about alternate treatments such as medication and relaxation.

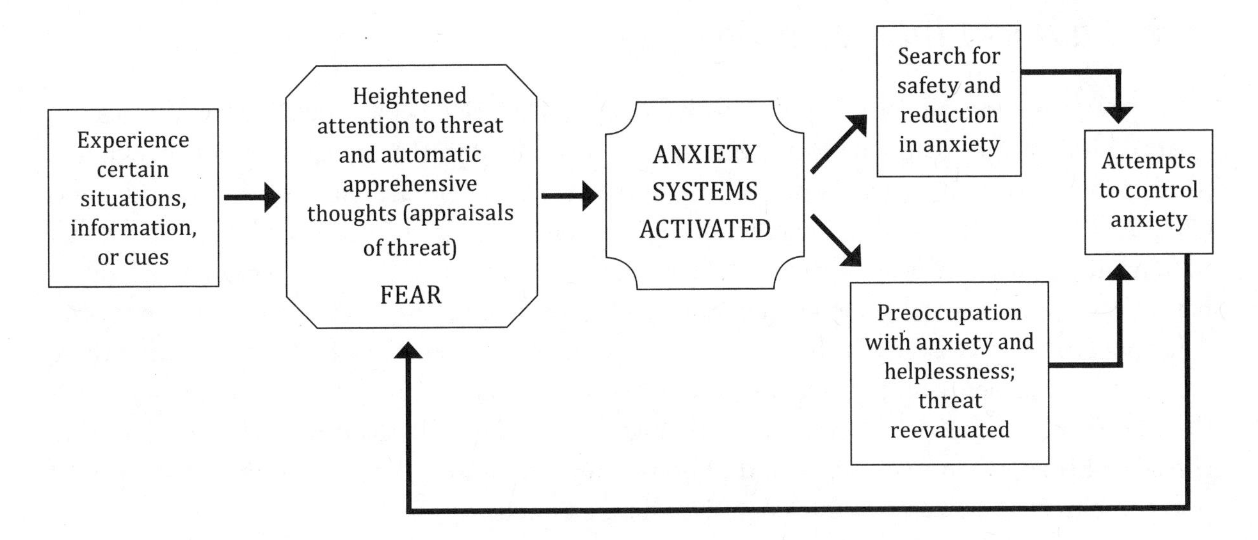

Figure 5.2 Simplified Diagram of the Cognitive Model of Anxiety
From *Cognitive Therapy of Anxiety Disorders* (p. 193), by D. A. Clark and A. T. Beck, 2010, New York: The Guilford Press. Adapted with permission.

Self-monitoring and identification of anxious thoughts is the second cognitive intervention, with in-session activities and out-of-session homework being utilized to help the anxious individual catch automatic thoughts, images, and appraisals that lead to anxiety. This skill is an important prerequisite to the third intervention.

Cognitive restructuring is that third intervention and a cornerstone of Clark and Beck's (2010) model. Several activities facilitate this restructuring, beginning with evidence gathering for and against the individual's beliefs about anxiety and the feared stimulus. A cost-benefit analysis of the current approach to dealing with it leads to more receptivity to change, and that is furthered by work on decatastrophizing thoughts about anxiety and what might happen. The client is guided into skills at identifying cognitive errors and generating alternatives, with the process climaxing with empirically testing new hypotheses with behavioral experiments, which might include exposure.

Clark and Beck (2010) make room for other techniques, such as imaginal reprocessing of past experiences of anxiety, with this applicable largely to past traumatic experiences, though often it is useful with other types of anxious experience. Writing about one's deepest thoughts and feelings about an emotional upset can also produce positive effects (see, for example, Gortner, Rude, & Pennebaker, 2006; Pennebaker, 1997). Clark and Beck (2010) also see potential benefit from notions of mindfulness, acceptance, and commitment, concepts we will explore in some detail in Chapters 6 and 7.

Behavioral Interventions

In their cognitive model, Clark and Beck (2010) are clear that behavioral interventions play an essential role in the treatment of anxiety. Yet, there is a reason the model does not include the word "behavioral" in its name. While this is not true of all models of cognitive behavioral therapy, Clark and Beck see behavioral interventions as serving to change threat-related cognition rather than having a purely behavioral purpose of habituating a person to an anxious response, or helping her unlearn or relearn behavioral conditioning. This means that the behavioral goals of exposure delineated in Chapter 2 are not the motivating factor in this model. That does not mean that these behavioral principles behind the effectiveness of exposure and response prevention do not work in the Clark and Beck model, but that those changes are not the purpose of the exposures. So, as we consider this approach to exposure and response prevention, we will focus on the added value of how these treatments can promote cognitive change as well.

EXPOSURE INTERVENTIONS

The reasons Clark and Beck (2010) include exposure in cognitive therapy include its being a way to learn more about the person's anxiety response as it is evoked in the situations normally avoided. It also provides a corrective experience of disconfirming the perception of threat and vulnerability and of testing catastrophic beliefs and affirming more adaptive appraisals and beliefs. It weakens reliance on safety cues and behaviors while reinforcing more adaptive coping strategies. It promotes the reduction of escape and avoidance behavior. Butler, Fennell, and Hackmann (2008) also argue that exposures activate "hot material" (p. 88), which can lead to spontaneous cognitive change.

Drawing on the work of Foa and Kozak (1986), Clark and Beck (2010) cite two essential aspects of exposure. First, to be therapeutic it must activate fear schemas to a point where the person is moderately anxious. Second, it must provide the person with information that disconfirms the maladaptive beliefs and cognitions. So, the person must attend to disconfirming information, including realizing the threat and sense of vulnerability are exaggerated.

Doing exposure properly is critical for treatment, for "probably no other psychotherapeutic intervention has been misjudged more often than exposure-based treatment" (Clark & Beck, 2010, p. 239). While the principles are relatively straightforward, actually implementing it properly with a therapeutic amount of exposure is challenging. Consistent with our discussion in Chapter 4, Clark and Beck assert that providing a satisfactory rationale for doing exposure is an essential prerequisite, emphasizing to the client that experience is key to changing emotion-based thought processes.

A hierarchy of situations for the exposure should be developed, very much as I described in chapter 4. Clark and Beck (2010) think it important that the therapist begin by supervising some exposures in session so that the client's response can be monitored and the client can be coached through it. Then, exposures are assigned as homework. They note that most therapists move through exposures sequentially beginning with moderately distressing situations and moving briskly up the hierarchy, the key being to move through it as rapidly as feasible. Clients keep records not only of the exposures, but on how exposures empirically test hypotheses about the actual nature and severity of the threats.

Clark and Beck (2010) concede that the literature is unclear as to the best approach to frequency and duration of exposures, but they suggest that exposures should be at least daily when this is the primary treatment modality, since insufficient practice may negatively affect the response to treatment. They concur with the literature (for example, Foa & Kozak, 1986) that cognitive distractions should be avoided during exposures. That is, clients should not be encouraged to imagine themselves elsewhere, cognitively distort or otherwise minimize fearful images, or even focus on nonfearful aspects of the situation, as these can reduce the activation of fear necessary for the exposures to do their work. While distraction may not be harmful in the short term, it may undermine the efficacy of treatment in the longer term. Clients are encouraged to attend to fear elements, minimize distraction, and not fight with their anxiety by trying to suppress their feelings (see Antony & Swinson, 2000). We will consider this issue further in Chapter 7.

How long should the exposure continue? The behavioral model (summarized in Chapter 4) argues that clients should persevere until the wave of anxiety subsides (*habituation*). However, if one uses a theory of exposure that says that it works by increasing a sense of self-efficacy or by incorporating more safety signals, then controlled escape (carefully easing out rather than using problematic escape strategies) is permissible if the anxiety becomes unbearable (Craske & Barlow, 2001). Clark and Beck (2010) question this: from their cognitive model's perspective, controlled escape might reinforce incorrect beliefs about the amount of actual danger in the situation. They therefore recommend staying with exposures until anxiety levels go back down. Using friends, family, or even the therapist for support in the very early stages of exposure therapy may help individuals endure exposures. Any such support should only be for the short term lest it become another avoidance behavior and undermine treatment. One option is to actually add partner-assisted exposure as a step in the hierarchy.

Cognitive strategies for managing anxious thinking may be helpful to facilitate persistence through exposures, and Clark and Beck (2010) suggest four. First, cognitive restructuring encourages the individual to note evidence in the situation that supports developing more realistic thoughts of how dangerous the situation actually is. Relaxation training is another technique that affords the person a coping strategy in the midst of exposures. Various forms might include controlled breathing, deep muscle relaxation, or meditative techniques. Sometimes paradoxical intention is a third approach: the client is encouraged to intentionally exaggerate the fear response and thus make its irrationality more evident. Calling a friend or even the therapist is a fourth, though this should be used quite judiciously. Finally, Clark and Beck (2010) advocate using a variety of exposures, consistent with our discussion of these in Chapter 4.

Cognitive behavioral therapy, then, utilizes exposure. In some forms, it relies on the behavioral mechanism discussed in Chapter 2, but by adding cognitive components, it refocuses exposures to be opportunities to test faulty thinking about dangers and to disprove them. While the behavioral mechanism of habituation may still be at work, cognitive changes are added to the motive and outcome of exposure in CBT.

RESPONSE PREVENTION

For Clark and Beck (2010), response prevention is "any therapeutic intervention that seeks to suppress the expression of safety-seeking responses in the context of anxiety arousal" (p. 251). It serves to help clients become more aware of their avoidance and escape behaviors, suppress these, and engage in more adaptive actions by staying exposed to feared stimuli. The intervention is particularly relevant in treatment of obsessive-compulsive disorder in tandem with exposure treatments, and its goal is to prevent inappropriate coping responses. It fits into the cognitive model during the elaborative phase where the person may seek to react to anxious activation by acting to escape the anxiety.

Like the cognitive adaptation of exposure, response prevention is used primarily in service of changing thinking. This is accomplished by recognizing faulty appraisals and beliefs regarding anxiety and acting according to more adaptive cognitions by facing the feared stimulus and tolerating the resultant anxiety until it subsides. Only by acting on new beliefs and appraisals can the client truly incorporate them into cognitive schema to alter the activation of anxiety.

Response prevention begins with identifying the cognitive, behavioral, or emotional responses that allow escape from exposure to feared stimuli. The therapist should talk these through with the client, but should also use behavioral experiments to observe the client and discover if there are some avoidant responses of which the client is unaware. The rationale for exposure and response prevention is then explained to the client, including the fact that stopping these responses will result in greater anxiety for a period of time.

Clark and Beck (2010) offer several strategies that promote successful response prevention. First, the therapist may give self-instructional coping statements to clients for use when they are resisting escape behaviors; these statements remind clients of the benefits of the intervention and the negative consequences of surrendering to the safety behavior. Second, competing activities might be assigned for use during the anxious moments. Individuals who ask questions to seek reassurance might instead be instructed to ask a friend about how he is feeling rather than asking questions for reassurance. Someone who compulsively washes her hands might be instructed to walk out on the porch instead of toward the bathroom.

The third blocking strategy is paradoxical intention, wherein the client is instructed to do the opposite of the safety behavior. Someone who fears crossing bridges would be directed to map out a new route to work that intentionally goes over bridges. A person with social anxiety disorder might be instructed to order items by phone rather than over the Internet. Clark and Beck (2010) believe paradoxical intention to be the most effective of the blocking strategies. The fourth strategy is the encouragement of friends and family; for example, a person with generalized anxiety who asks multiple questions about possible problems might ask her friend to gently ask her in return, "Would it be better if I didn't answer your question?"

More than just preventing responses, the cognitive model of Clark and Beck (2010) supports the development of more adaptive coping responses, which include anything that allows the anxiety to subside naturally rather than in response to escape behaviors. Part of developing these responses will be to identify and challenge the verity of any problematic beliefs associated with the avoidance or escape behavior.

Response prevention fits neatly into CBT for its basic behavioral effects, but also as a means of identifying more maladaptive thoughts and proving experientially that those thoughts are not true. In so doing, new beliefs are established that can change appraisals of future events, reducing the frequency of the activation of threat mode.

CHAPTER 6

Exposure in the Context of Dialectical Behavior Therapy

Cognitive behavioral therapy (CBT) has garnered both empirical support and popularity among therapists. But it has not been without its critics. A complaint voiced by many counselors is that CBT is insensitive and unaccepting: it focuses on finding the wrong thinking in which the client is trapped, obviously implying that he is, well, wrong to think that way. Cognitive behavioral therapy has always acknowledged the importance of the therapeutic relationship (Beck, 2011), yet the stereotype has often been that CBT is merely a rational, logical undertaking. If we consider our focus on exposure therapy (ET), where people who often have spent years trying to avoid feared situations are invited to do the very thing they have struggled to escape, it may seem even more heartless.

It is therefore easy for the anxious individual to feel disheartened at a CBT approach to her problems, even if the literature shows it will help. How many of us know diet and exercise will help us lose weight, but struggle to do the unpleasant work? It is no wonder that CBT, and ET in particular, experiences numerous therapy dropouts.

As difficult as making needed changes may be for persons with excessive anxiety, it is much more at issue with more severely disturbed persons who are chronically suicidal and/or suffering from borderline personality disorder (BPD). This was the dilemma that Marsha Linehan faced (Swales & Heard, 2009) as she considered using CBT with this population. She realized they needed a radical acceptance, beyond the change that CBT could provide. Her project to resolve this dilemma grew into dialectical behavior therapy (DBT; Linehan, 1993a, 1993 b).

In this chapter I will briefly summarize DBT's philosophical foundations and their incorporation into a model of therapy. I will introduce the main types of strategies and skills used in DBT with an eye to how they apply to anxiety disorders, and particularly how they relate to ET. I'll conclude by speaking to how ET is incorporated into DBT and making some suggestions on incorporating relevant aspects of DBT into more traditional ET.

A Brief Introduction to the Fundamental Principles of DBT

Linehan was very conscious of the struggles of those with serious and persistent mental illness and sought ways to provide better therapy for this population. Her Catholic faith provided her with an experience that sparked the core construct of DBT: radical acceptance.

Mindfulness

Linehan looked to the East, rather than to conceptions Western psychology offered, for a fuller understanding of acceptance. She learned that acceptance is accepting what is in the present moment and that accepting oneself includes accepting who one is at this moment, not simply some ideal that may or may not be achieved. Linehan (1993a) incorporated this Zen philosophy of accepting life as it is in the moment into her approach to therapy, fully realizing that achieving such would be a true challenge to persons suffering from serious mental illness. Mindfulness (Swales & Heard, 2009) offers a set of skills to facilitate this radical acceptance, and exercises teaching these are woven throughout DBT. We will revisit mindfulness shortly.

Behavioral Techniques

Despite drawing from Eastern thought, Linehan (1993a) is still a trained Western psychologist, and she also built her model on the data supporting CBT. Her focus is more on behavioral techniques than cognitive ones, as she sees all behaviors, adaptive or not, as having been influenced by prior learning (Reynolds & Linehan, 2002). Operant conditioning, for example, is valued in DBT, though therapists are encouraged to analyze behavior carefully and not assume that initial impressions betray what actually acts as a reinforcer or punisher in a specific context for a specific person (Swales & Heard, 2009). Along with other third-wave therapies, DBT applies operant principles to thoughts, not just behaviors. Thoughts of suicide, for example, are negatively reinforcing as they ease emotional pain by considering the cessation of that pain in death.

Swales and Heard (2009) also observe that DBT utilizes classical conditioning. Dialectical behavior therapy sees anxiety, for example, as often learned from the association of cues related to events of trauma—which is found quite often in the history of those with BPD. While DBT considers such learning to occur in other contexts as well, such an understanding of anxiety as classically conditioned gives exposure a place in DBT.

Dialectics

Linehan faced a dilemma. As we saw, behavioral techniques are about change and thus are in an important sense not accepting of the client. In contrast, mindfulness can produce radical acceptance. However, even teaching mindfulness to aid in accepting the moment exposes a lack of acceptance as well, for it does not accept the client's wishes to change. How could she reconcile a technology of behavior change and the idea of radical acceptance into a coherent whole? Linehan (1993a) found her answer in dialectical philosophy, which sees the world as a progression of theses and antitheses that are resolved into syntheses. Dialectics are something like paradoxes, but their seemingly contradictory elements can be integrated in some sense. This process plays out in DBT to allow both therapist and client to maintain flexibility and balance (Koerner & Dimeff, 2007).

The dialectic of acceptance and change is resolved in what Linehan (1993a) calls "validation," where the therapist accepts the client, including those of her responses that need to be changed. Those responses are considered to be sensible given the client's current life situation and thus are accepted while still opening the door to change. The client's coping is accepted as understandable under the circumstances, but so is her wanting to change to find more flexible and adaptive ways of coping, and this is also accepted.

Dialectics play out in many ways in DBT that we will not be able to cover, but to illustrate we introduce one: client dialectics, aspects of functioning that appear to contradict but that may be synthesized. Moonshine (2008) offers some helpful examples of these, such as not wanting to change but not wanting to be in pain, wanting to be better but still engaging in self-destructive behavior, and wanting life to be easy but doing things that make it harder. Such dialectics are targets for the skills taught in DBT, which sees the dialectic of moving between extremes of emotion and behavior as another key dialectic for those with BPD (Reynolds & Linehan, 2002).

Biosocial Theory and Focus on Emotion

Linehan (1993a) sees the critical aspect of BPD as a broader failure of the emotion regulation system. This failure stems from and is maintained by biological and social systems. Biologically, Linehan argues that persons with BPD have central nervous systems that render it more difficult to regulate emotions and thus they have more frequent and intense affective reactions than many others. When an individual with these challenges is placed in a thoroughly invalidating environment, problems are almost inevitable. For example, people may misunderstand this emotional dyscontrol and respond inappropriately or minimize its seriousness. For many with BPD, being sexually abused in childhood was part of this invalidating environment. The long-term result is the individual's inability to effectively regulate her emotions.

The person with poor emotion regulation will be impacted in three ways (Reynolds & Linehan, 2002): being overly sensitive to emotional stimuli; being highly reactive to emotional stimuli; and being slow to return to an emotional baseline after being stimulated. These provide foci for therapy as skills are learned to better manage these. While persons with anxiety disorders most often have not been sexually abused, certainly there is often a challenge in their ability to regulate emotion, and that is a requisite ability to tolerating exposure.

Ideas from Broader Social Science Research

The sources for DBT are not limited to psychotherapy studies, but freely draw from a broader literature offering concepts and techniques that are helpful (Swales & Heard, 2009). We have already seen how Buddhist teachings are fundamental to DBT, but Linehan (1993a) also borrows from areas such as crisis management and social psychology. Swales and Heard (2009) illustrate this, citing DBT's stress on the client making an explicit commitment to treatment and citing research saying that this increases people's likelihood of remaining in a situation. Given the nature of BPD and its reactivity, getting such a treatment commitment is a logical application of the theory.

DBT by the Numbers

Dialectical behavior therapy views the treatment process itself as a type of dialectic, and there is not a rigid session-by-session manual for how treatment is to proceed, though it is topically structured to an extent. Treatment will be a "thesis" that faces "antitheses" as new information comes to light and the client's life changes, and DBT moves to be the dialectical synthesis of approaches and context. Below, I will summarize the key dimensions that form the structure of Linehan's approach.

Five Functions of Treatment

Given the complexities of BPD, for which DBT was developed, targets for treatment are prioritized according to how threatening certain things are to the client's quality of life (Koerner & Dimeff, 2007), yet overall the strategies and interventions of DBT serve five functions (Salsman, 2008). Given the problematic biological and social histories that are theorized to lie behind BPD, therapists will first work to *resolve deficits in behavioral skills* through broadening the client's behavioral skills repertoire. Those with BPD may have a history of failing in relationships, life, and even therapy. A second function of treatment is to *remove blocks that hinder therapy* and to *reinforce effective behaviors*. This has clear application to helping clients through exposure and response prevention as well.

Drawing again on its behavioral roots, DBT's third function is to *facilitate generalization of new skills* into the real world of clients' lives. Dialectical behavior therapy has a broader aspect that borders on social work in that it, as a fourth goal, seeks to alter clients' environments by *intervening so as to maximize therapy gains*. Working with borderline clients can be exhausting, as can most forms of psychotherapy; DBT does not overlook this and has as a final function of therapy to *enhance the capabilities and motivation of the therapist*.

These broad objectives work themselves out through the levels of disorder and the corresponding stages of treatment.

Four Levels of Disorder and Stages of Treatment

In her initial major work on DBT, Linehan (1993a) posited two stages of treatment that followed a pretreatment phase, though she later (1999) developed this into four stages that coincide with levels of disorder, broadening the use of DBT beyond BPD.

Like most forms of CBT, DBT begins with a pretreatment stage where client and therapist agree to goals and methods for treatment (Koerner & Dimeff, 2007). Collaboration is very important in DBT, and commitment to the agreement is stressed, to increase the likelihood of the client persevering should therapy become challenging. Beyond this, the beginning point of therapy will depend on the severity of disorder.

Level 1 disorders are the most severe and pervasive, marked by significant lack of control of behaviors (Reynolds & Linehan, 2002), with suicidality or other life-threatening events being the first priority (Koerner & Dimeff, 2007). Stage 1 treatment thus focuses on these severe symptoms, with the hierarchy moving from the aforementioned suicidal behaviors, to reducing client and therapist behaviors that might interfere with treatment, to reducing behavior patterns that interfere with the quality of life, to acquiring skills to meet goals, to other goals the client wishes to address (Reynolds & Linehan, 2002). This is standard DBT and is the form that has been the focus of most of the research.

If Level 1 disorder is "loud desperation" then Level 2 is "quiet desperation" (Reynolds & Linehan, 2002, p. 624), as the central problem is avoidance of emotion and any cues associated with it. Clients with post-traumatic stress disorder (PTSD) are prototypical of this level of disorder, and Stage 2 treatment has as its objective to increase the person's ability to experience emotions without distress. Stated differently, Stage 2 is about exposing the client to strong emotions and situations that evoke them, giving exposure therapy a place within DBT (Becker & Zayfert, 2001). Koerner and Dimeff (2007, p. 6) note that "DBT encourages acquisition of skills to a sufficient level that one has a reasonable quality of life/stability of behavioral control prior to systematic exposure to cues that are associated with past trauma." In so doing, DBT takes the feared memories/situations into the context of broader pathology than just the anxiety itself. It is critical to note that many persons benefit from a focus on stability prior to entering into exposure, a need DBT makes explicit. We will consider more of how exposure fits in Stage 2 later in this chapter.

Level 3 problems are basically patterns of behavior that interfere with the client's goals and may include problems in employment, education, or marriage. Stage 3 DBT responds by focusing on building ordinary happiness and self-respect (Reynolds & Linehan, 2002). Level 4 disorder is a remaining sense of incompleteness despite a basic satisfaction with the quality of life. Stage 4 DBT treats this by increasing the person's capacity for consistent happiness through psychological insights, an expanded awareness of self, and spiritual practices. In general, DBT thus moves from the outside in, from overt behaviors to more psychologically minded well-being, beginning at the level of functioning determined in pretreatment. Interventions along the way are drawn from four broad categories.

Four Groups of Treatment Strategies

Dialectical behavior therapy is quite systematic in addressing all problematic behaviors presented by the client, doing so in the context of a strong therapeutic relationship, which is considered essential to change (Reynolds & Linehan, 2002). The DBT model has a number of specific protocols for certain common problems (suicidality, crises, and so on), but its strategies generally fall into four categories.

Dialectical strategies begin with the central focus of balancing acceptance and change. These techniques are dispersed throughout treatment as it tries to expose to consciousness opposites that are then synthesized. Among these techniques are storytelling and the use of ambiguity.

Core strategies (Reynolds & Linehan, 2002) include problem-solving and validation strategies, which are balanced in treatment. The former are taken largely from behavior therapy and include exposure in the effort to target maladaptive behaviors. In DBT, the behaviors are analyzed and accepted prior to seeking alternate solutions to problem situations.

The change of problem-solving strategies is balanced by acceptance, which is accomplished through validation strategies. In DBT, validation occurs through the therapist accepting the client and communicating that acceptance effectively to her. Much of validation is found in the fundamental therapeutic skills of unconditional positive regard and building rapport, but moves on to "deeper" acceptance of aspects of the client that are unspoken. Understanding the client's situation in light of past learning and biological predispositions is also a form of validation, as is treating the client as having equal status in treatment as the therapist.

Communication strategies are twofold in DBT (Reynolds & Linehan, 2002) and these require delicate balancing by the therapist. The baseline approach to communication is reciprocal, which includes being warm and responsive to the client's agenda. However, on some occasions an irreverent style is used that is humorous or even a bit outrageous as it addresses the client's hidden assumptions or draws out overlooked implications of the client's behavior. Reynolds and Linehan (2002, p. 626) illustrate this by saying that if a client were to say, "I am going to kill myself," the therapist might reply, "But I thought you agreed not to drop out of therapy!" This must be skillfully balanced with reciprocal communication to achieve the optimal change in treatment.

Case management strategies are threefold and guide the counselor on interactions outside the actual sessions. The consultation-to-the-client strategy manifests the principle that the therapist teaches the client to deal more successfully with his or her context, rather than making the context adapt to him or her. On occasion the therapist may be required to act in the client's environment to protect the client or assist in areas where the client lacks influence (environmental intervention). Finally, the consultation-to-the-therapist strategy requires the counselor to meet regularly with a supervisor or consultation team, this also serving to aid the counselor in appropriately balancing the first two strategies.

Four Modes of Treatment in DBT

Linehan (1993a) uses the term "mode" to describe each of the four core components of standard DBT treatment. The first and foundational mode is individual outpatient psychotherapy, and the individual therapist serves as leader of the client's treatment team. Individual therapy is weekly, though it may be more frequent during rough patches. Also, sometimes sessions longer than the traditional fifty-minute hour are in order. Remaining in individual therapy is a requirement for participating in the other modes.

Dialectical behavior therapy is well known for teaching skills, and much of this work is done in skills training groups so that individual therapy can focus more on suicidal and borderline behaviors. Skills are taught in psychoeducational groups that meet for two to two-and-a-half hours each week (or in two one-hour sessions) and are preferably not led by the individual therapist. There are four primary skills modules, focusing on mindfulness, interpersonal effectiveness, emotion regulation, and distress tolerance (we look more closely at these in the section that follows). Detailed guidelines for these groups are found in Linehan's (1993b) widely used manual for group leaders. Once skills are learned, clients may transition into supportive process groups and must stay in individual therapy as well.

For several important reasons, DBT encourages phone calls between the client and the individual therapist between sessions (Linehan, 1993a). This may give those with BPD more effective ways to deal with crises than parasuicidal or self-defeating behaviors. These phone calls also aid with generalization of behavioral skills as they are used in the environment (and thus exposure therapy in the DBT context may include a component of walking through exposures with clients by phone). Linehan also sees the calls as offering an occasion for client and therapist to reconcile when there was conflict or misunderstanding in the session.

Finally, as DBT was developed for borderline patients, therapists are strongly encouraged to be in regular case consultation meetings. Persons with BPD can put much pressure on therapists to vary therapy when it should not be varied, or lead them to react by being rigid when some flexibility was in order. Consultation groups afford support and guidance to therapists working with challenging populations.

Four Sets of Skills

Linehan (1993b) organizes skills needed to overcome mental distress and behavior problems into four areas, each comprising a section for the groups to cover. Moonshine (2008) offers a briefer and more recent summary of these, which you might consult. I will cover these in a way that anticipates our discussion of exposure therapy in DBT.

CORE MINDFULNESS SKILLS

Linehan (1993b) calls these "core" because they are so central to DBT. She sees persons as being in one of three "minds." A "reasonable mind" is when the person is thinking rationally and is planful, and is cool and deliberate in her plans. A person is in her "emotion mind" when her emotions are largely in control of her thinking and her cognitions are "hot." In keeping with dialectics, these poles are integrated into a "wise mind," which honors thinking and feeling, but also adds a degree of intuition. This balance is achieved through mindfulness.

Anxious persons share in common with those with BPD a tendency to live in the future or past, avoiding fears from the past and worrying to prevent unpleasant events in the future. Drawing focus into the present is thus helpful for both groups.

Mindfulness *"what" skills* help develop a sense of participating in the present moment with awareness. Consider how we often eat: distracted by our thoughts and the environment, we rarely actually savor the food we are consuming. The first of these "what" skills, then, is to observe what is happening now without trying to change it—even if it is unpleasant (like an anxious thought). Second, individuals learn skills to describe these events, such as describing the sensations in one's belly rather than just saying "I'm scared." Finally, the person learns to participate in the ongoing moment without self-consciousness.

The *"how" skills* of mindfulness enable the client to attend to, describe, and participate in a nonjudgmental way: the feeling in one's stomach is neither good nor bad. The person also learns to be aware of only one thing in the moment, focusing the mind rather than splitting attention. Finally, mindfulness involves being effective by doing what works, not what one might insist is "right." For persons with anxiety, this might mean going to a friend's house for dinner even if it is frightening and even though the individual will be mindful of anxious feelings and sensations along the way, as this "works" for the goal of deepening relationships.

INTERPERSONAL EFFECTIVENESS SKILLS

Linehan (1993b) understands that those with BPD may have good interpersonal skills but struggle in applying the right skill to the right situation. This second set of skills is akin to most assertiveness and interpersonal problem-solving skills, with a slight change of focus. In DBT, "effectiveness" means "obtaining changes one wants, maintaining the relationship, and maintaining your self-respect" (p. 70). A basic dialectic addressed by these skills is the movement back and forth between intense confrontation and utter avoidance of conflict, or discerning when to accept something and when to try to change it. Part of the tension is a tendency to prematurely end relationships, a trend likely due to skills deficits in the other areas (inability to tolerate distress in relationships, challenges in regulating the emotions of anger or frustration, a lack of skill in attending to the moment nonjudgmentally, and a shortage of the problem-solving skills needed to navigate potential relationship conflict).

An example of the practical skills taught here is the "DEAR MAN" acronym (Linehan, 1993b). This entails Describing the situation without judgment, Expressing feelings about the situation clearly, Asserting wishes, Reinforcing those who cooperate with you, staying Mindful of your objectives in the situation without distraction, Appearing confident, and Negotiating when necessary. Such skills are easily translated for use with those with social anxiety or shyness and can enhance the confidence they manifest when exposing themselves to anxiety-evoking situations such as meeting people, going on job interviews, or asking for a raise. These can thus enhance exposures to certain types of fears.

EMOTION REGULATION SKILLS

We noted earlier Linehan's (1993a) model of emotional vulnerability due to biology and history. This theory offers validation for the individual's ineffectiveness in regulating emotion and paves the way for teaching skills to overcome this challenge. Linehan (1993b) makes clear that teaching these skills to those with BPD is a challenge and must be done in the context of their having emotional self-validation.

Skills taught in this module include identifying and labeling emotions, identifying challenges to changing emotions, reducing vulnerability to "emotion mind," increasing positive emotional events, taking the opposite action for the emotion, and applying distress tolerance techniques. This last set of skills shows the fourth module to be essentially a subset of emotion regulation (Swales & Heard, 2009).

Another skill in emotion regulation is increasing mindfulness to current emotions (Linehan, 1993b), which I single out for its relevance to exposure. Here the client is taught to use mindfulness to stay with emotion in the present moment without judging or trying to block or inhibit them. When one judges current feelings as "bad," it can lead to secondary emotions that cascade into emotional turmoil. This is a common process in anxiety, for recognizing sensations as meaning one is "anxious" can, for many, lead into a "fear of fear," in which feeling anxious may forebode a panic attack or bout of emesis. Thus, these skills have great relevance to people with panic disorders or even generalized anxiety disorder.

DISTRESS TOLERANCE SKILLS

Most of mental health practice is built on the idea of eliminating unpleasantnesses: ridding the patient of distressing emotions or unhappy circumstances. Hayes, Strosahl, and Wilson (2011) begin their book on acceptance and commitment therapy by making a convincing case that the field has erred in this regard, for suffering is an inevitable aspect of life; but Linehan (1993a, 1993b) can be credited for recognizing this problem early on. Linehan sees the ability to tolerate distress as an outworking of mindfulness, acknowledging religious and spiritual traditions have long understood that some suffering is inevitable and the key is to bear it skillfully rather than to avoid it. So, tolerating and accepting distress becomes a vital mental health goal.

Tolerating distress amounts to accepting oneself and one's situation in a nonevaluative manner, doing so without putting demands on the situation or one's emotions to be different than they are. In DBT, this skill focuses on managing crises and life as it comes. Two sets of skills are taught in this module. The first set includes skills that empower the person to cope with crises, including distracting, self-soothing, improving the moment, and thinking of the pros and cons (Linehan, 1993b).

The second set is more relevant to exposure therapy and includes acceptance skills such as complete acceptance from deep within (radical acceptance), choosing to accept reality as it is, and moving from willfulness to willingness, a concept drawn from Gerald May (1982). *Willingness* is grasping that one is part of a process larger than oneself and a commitment to live within that process. This may follow from one's spiritual or religious beliefs, but also can be a more existential understanding of life as it is. In contrast, willfulness is fighting with things as they are as one tries to control what is beyond control. Thus willingness is not surrender, or even a passive stance, as it requires standing against destructive forces even as it accepts what is in the moment.

This is a vital point for our exploration of exposure therapy, as those with anxiety are commonly inclined to willfully control their circumstances to avoid experiencing the sensations and thoughts of anxiety. Exposure asks the person to sit with those sensations and thoughts to allow them to subside, but may offer no clear rationale for doing so other than its being yet another way to control them. Distress tolerance offers a mind-set that decreases the tendency to fight the feelings incurred in exposure, and so makes exposure more doable. While habituation will occur, that is no longer the goal, but merely an incidental benefit from learning to accept the natural discomforts of life.

Therapists who would like to teach DBT skills without using the entire model of DBT can find helpful exercises for the four skill groups in McKay, Wood, and Brantley (2007). Now we turn to consider the place of exposure in DBT more specifically.

DBT and Exposure Therapy

A number of the concepts, strategies, and techniques of DBT have relevance to exposure therapy, but exposure is also an explicit set of techniques in DBT (Linehan, 1993a). We will look at how DBT uses exposure strategies in its overall plan before considering when and how therapists might "borrow" some aspects of DBT to help in certain types of exposure therapy.

Exposure-Based Procedures in DBT

I'll begin by noting that DBT sees exposure as relevant to a broader range of negative emotions than just fear and anxiety (Linehan, 1993a; Swales & Heard, 2009), with guilt, shame, and anger being other emotions that may be modulated through exposure skills. These activities are not a formal module in DBT, with the exception of Stage 2 treatment of PTSD and sexual abuse in particular—though Linehan (1993a) indicates that the DBT method can be replaced by any well-developed model of exposure in such cases. Swales and Heard (2009) also note that DBT uses exposure to deal with in-session affect. Rather than use avoidance behaviors such as changing the subject, DBT encourages therapist and client alike to stay with the emotion as it occurs in the moment.

Linehan (1993a) weaves exposure throughout therapy, but still sees it as having five rudimentary steps: finding appropriate stimuli that elicit the emotional response; not reinforcing the emotional response (and this would potentially include response prevention, which negatively reinforces the affective response); leading into the third step, which is blocking avoidance and escape behaviors. Even in imaginal exposure, the therapist should guide the client to stay with the present and not avoid emotion through wandering attention, avoiding fear, hiding shame, and so on. Dialectical behavior therapy also sees enhancing the client's sense of control as important, as evidenced in these skills to manage attention and allocation of the thought process (this is the fourth step), as is ensuring that the exposure is long enough and happens often enough to do its job (the fifth step).

In DBT, collaboration and buy-in from the client are important if exposure is to be successful. Linehan expands on the tolerance of affect in exposure to include working to change the emotion experienced when exposed to the threatening stimulus. She thus encourages clients to use postures and facial expressions that contradict the fear to facilitate communicating to the brain that the situation is not so frightening after all. The therapist may explicitly teach the client different postures of body for expression of emotion that more realistically reflect the moment than panicked or shameful postures during the experience of affect.

Exposure (Linehan, 1993a) should be done so that it does not recreate the original trauma or anxiety, but adds new information about safety. For instance, successfully exposing a person to a dog requires that the dog not snap at the person. Moreover, the exposure situation must match the problem context so that the problematic affect is elicited. Linehan encourages graded exposure, moving from low intensity to high. Keys to an effective exposure, as we noted earlier, are eliciting a sufficient amount of the negative emotion, letting the client choose to terminate the exposure without using avoidance behaviors, and persisting until the client feels a lowering of the unpleasant emotion.

In DBT, exposure is also a part of other exercises, as they may evoke negative emotions. For example, saying no to someone might evoke anxiety or guilt. Here the exposure may be in service of learning interpersonal effectiveness skills. Mindfulness is another place where exposure occurs naturally, as the individual stays with and accepts discomfort in the moment. However, the inverse also holds true, for learning to accept the emotion enhances the ability to tolerate exposure. So, exposure and mindfulness exercises can work together hand in glove.

Borrowing from DBT to Enhance Exposure Therapy

Dialectical behavior therapy has proven itself to be helpful for BPD and parasuicidal behaviors, and also has research to support its efficacy in substance abuse, bulimia, binge eating, and depression in the elderly (Koerner & Dimeff, 2007), as well as PTSD, though the outcome research to date is equivocal on PTSD (Cahill, Rothbaum, Resick, & Follette, 2009). It also promises to help those who are anxious; for example, Marra (2004) has authored a helpful workbook for clients who can benefit from adapting DBT skills and strategies for their anxious symptoms. In this section, we will consider a model for integrating DBT into traditional ET for PTSD developed by Becker and Zayfert (2001) and summarize some other informal ways DBT can enhance ET and RP.

SUPPLEMENTING CBT-BASED EXPOSURE WITH DBT

Dialectical behavior therapy is not, of course, designed for anxiety disorders, and for the most part, anxiety disorders are not as severe as BPD and chronic suicidality, the main targets of the therapy. Most people struggling with excessive anxiety do not need such intensive treatment nor all the skills taught in DBT. However, anxiety is often a part of BPD, and anxiety disorders do not preclude the presence of some of the more severe symptoms of BPD. Post-traumatic stress disorder has already been mentioned as one of the more severe anxiety disorders that have been treated using DBT approaches, and it is a diagnosis most likely to benefit from DBT skills.

Becker and Zayfert (2001) developed a model for tying their more traditional exposure-based treatment for PTSD to DBT, affording a look at one way DBT can supplement ET. The authors begin with differential diagnosis, and if the client with PTSD is also clearly diagnosed with BPD, then he is referred to a DBT program if it's available; the client is asked to return to their group for PTSD treatment once the DBT program is completed. Should such a program not be available near the client, then their group would provide limited Stage 1 DBT treatment. This limited Stage 1 treatment is also offered to those with severe PTSD who are struggling to function adaptively in their environments until the goals of Stage 1—reduced parasuicidal behaviors and better regulated emotion—are achieved. More specifically, Stage 1 helps strengthen their functioning until they are able to tolerate exposure, at which point they are moved back into a traditional CBT program using exposure therapy. Even at that point, some aspects and skills of DBT can be integrated. Some of the authors' thoughts on that follow.

DBT SKILLS TO IMPROVE EXPOSURE THERAPY

First, knowing DBT skills and how to teach them to clients can enhance therapists' confidence in assigning exposure exercises, as there are more tools with which to support the client in the exercise and cope with any struggles the client has in completing them. Cognitive behavioral therapists using DBT techniques benefit from viewing therapy as a dialectic between acceptance and change. This entails a stronger focus on acceptance and validating clients. Many CBT strategies, including ET and RP, can readily be seen as invalidating to struggling clients. Awareness of DBT helps the therapist intentionally validate the client's apprehension and inclination to escape anxious situations. One specific form of validation is showing flexibility to deal with current problems that arise (such as the death of a loved one or a job change) rather than feeling compelled to stick to the treatment manual one might be following.

As noted, exposure can be invalidating as well. Becker and Zayfert (2001) adapt to this by stressing the need for a decision analysis to precede exposure, helping clients assess the benefits of avoidance, validating it as a coping strategy, before shifting to see the negative effects of avoidance and escape behaviors. Such analysis can be applied throughout therapy to address the patient's hesitancy around exposure exercises. They also recommend adapting the collaborative model of DBT, where therapists consult other professionals to manage their own stresses and monitor the ethics of exposure. Moreover, they concur with Linehan (1993a) that phone conversations between sessions can be helpful to facilitate generalizing exposure skills into daily life.

As in DBT, Becker and Zayfert (2001) see exposure as a skill to be learned, not merely a technique to be implemented. Mindfulness skills equip the client to better focus attention on anxiety and thus tolerate the exposure better. Teaching skills to enhance radical acceptance also prepares clients better for tolerating the distress of exposure or being denied escape and avoidance responses.

Mindfulness is a most helpful skill in exposure. Distracting oneself from the anxiety during exposure may actually impede the effectiveness of it. Tolerating it mindfully can make exposure more effective. Helpful exercises for teaching mindfulness are available in McKay, Wood, and Brantley (2007) to teach the client to attend to present experience without moving focus to thoughts of things not immediate. For example, the counselor might ask the client to relax, close his eyes, and breathe slowly, then give the client a peppermint and have him attend carefully to the taste, physical sensations, and sounds associated with it, while also closely monitoring any emotional response without evaluating it. One can then move to doing a similar activity with the flow of thought, keeping it present-focused, while moving from being mindful of one's thinking to being mindful of a single object in the environment. Moving back and forth in one's attention helps develop the skill to experience life and emotions as a flow that one does not interrupt—an ability that serves exposures quite well.

Distress tolerance is another family of skills that are related to mindfulness and can help with exposure. As Linehan (1993b) notes, the wise mind is accepting. Skills helpful here include learning to improve the moment by imagining relaxing scenes; finding meaning in the moment; opening one's heart to God, a supreme being, or one's own wise mind for strength to bear up; relaxing; and thinking of only one thing in the moment. Several of these offer ways to cope with the distress of exposure. Self-soothing skills also promote the client's ability to manage affect in the midst of exposure and life in general. These include soothing each of the senses through finding and making beauty in sight, sound, smell, taste, and touch. Activities to promote these include watching a candle flame, listening to peaceful music, breathing in the smells of flowers, savoring a favorite food or drink, or taking a bubble bath. While these cannot be done during the exposures themselves, they offer both a respite from the distress of doing exposures and something to anticipate.

Closing Thoughts on DBT and Exposure

Linehan's (1993a) model explicitly includes exposure therapy and in less obvious ways addresses response prevention. Yet, overall the approach may be more than the average person suffering with anxiety needs. Any good initial evaluation needs to include possible suicidality and Axis II issues in addition to any individual symptoms that are often associated with the severe behaviors of BPD or other personality disorders. Even a simple phobia does not make one immune to more significant issues. If these more chronic and severe behaviors are evident, then DBT is an excellent choice and will be much more helpful than just doing exposure for the phobia.

Among the anxiety disorders, PTSD may be the most severe and thus have the most overlap with BPD. The careful strategy of Becker and Zayfert (2001), described above, offers a useful guide to whether DBT might be needed prior to exposure-based CBT. Moreover, some people lack the skills for exposure, even if they have no more severe diagnoses, and the careful therapist does well to identify these deficits and teach the corresponding skills to build a firmer foundation for more traditional ET and RP. In that regard, some pieces of DBT can help form a helpful initial treatment phase prior to the initiation of ET.

Yet, for the broader range of anxiety disorders, there is little research and maybe little need for such a comprehensive therapy. Nonetheless, much can be said for focusing on mechanisms that promote change rather than relying only on manualized programs. This approach opens the door to incorporating several key elements of DBT into treatment of all anxieties across the diagnostic spectrum. Central to that is the philosophical shift from controlling anxiety by avoiding it to a radical acceptance of the place of suffering and mindfulness of the normal discomforts of life. Much can also be said for a more careful acceptance of the anxious patient and his efforts to do his best in his current situation. Cognitive behavioral therapy can be, as we saw, quite invalidating. Dialectical behavior therapy also opens the door to considering ET for feelings other than anxiety, and to the secondary emotions caused by adverse reactions to feeling bad. This is especially true in panic disorder. Quite a few of the DBT skills can facilitate a better life for clients rather than merely teach them to regulate a fear, and these skills can also help entice clients to persevere through ET. For example, a stronger sense of interpersonal effectiveness can promote exposure to new social settings and help clients envision a better and happier life.

In fact, the one aspect that DBT might improve on is to deepen its focus on a better life for clients. It is here that acceptance and commitment therapy picks up the baton and moves the third wave of cognitive behavioral therapies into a realm rich in possibilities for those with anxiety.

CHAPTER 7

Exposure in the Context of Acceptance and Commitment Therapy

Exposure therapy (ET) offers much hope to those who experience excessive and inappropriate anxiety, but it is not an easy row to hoe. In its basic behavioral form, we saw that it is effective, but presents great challenges to therapist and client alike. For clients, it is intimidating to be asked to do the very thing that daunts them: face the dreaded thing head-on. After all, if they were willing to face their fears in the first place, they would not be in therapy. Anxiety is all about avoiding the feared thing/situation/thought, so what is the motivation to face it? Dropping out of treatment becomes a viable option in the minds of many anxious persons.

For therapists, this yields the challenging task of keeping clients invested in ET and motivating them to do the hard work of exposure. These difficulties detract from the success rate of ET, as it cannot work if it is not completed, and it cannot be completed unless the therapist-client team navigates these troubling waters successfully. How does one encourage a person with anxiety to face the very thing he works so diligently to avoid? Maybe he worries and avoids some things, but at least in doing so, the feared thing itself is largely escaped. Yet, we know the price for such escape in emotional suffering is too high. This is, after all, why an anxious individual comes for therapy: the work of avoiding anxiety only leads to more anxiety, in a most distressing spiral.

While "pure" ET has shown effectiveness, as discussed in Chapter 1, giving the behavioral technique a broader context can enhance its effectiveness. We saw that cognitive behavioral therapy (CBT) supplements the purely behavioral version of ET by offering cognitive rationales that fortify the client to do exposure and sustain her as she endures exposure. Mindfulness approaches may also be used in conjunction with CBT to lessen the intimidation of feeling anxious or facing anxious situations. Dialectical behavior therapy (DBT) puts mindfulness into a therapeutic context where broader skills equip the client with the ability to face anxiety-evoking events successfully, even though anxiety was not in the forefront in DBT's development.

We come now to acceptance and commitment therapy (ACT, pronounced as one word, "act"), whose theory and approach make it almost ideal for those with anxiety (Batten, 2011) in that it focuses on increasing willingness to accept what is and emphasizes moving past the experiential avoidance that is so characteristic of problematic anxiety. The shift away from control and effortful cognitive emotion regulation that is nascent in DBT is central to ACT (Eifert & Forsyth, 2005). Acceptance and commitment therapy builds on the history of CBT (and is thus part of the "third wave" of behavioral therapies) and improves upon it in important ways.

Eifert and Forsyth (2005) draw out several implications of the central CBT focus on mastery and control, and they illustrate how ACT takes anxiety treatment further. Clients often present in therapy hoping merely to be rid of the "symptoms" of anxiety, seeing those as the problem. Many therapists concur that these symptoms are the cause of the suffering associated with anxiety. In contrast, ACT emphasizes the larger issue of the person living life according to her values, with these symptoms derailing the sufferer from pursuit of these important goals.

Second, Eifert and Forsyth (2005) explain how it does not work for anxiety to be a symptom and the definition of a disorder simultaneously. A headache is not a disorder, but a symptom that hints at something going wrong behind it, be it the process of a migraine, problems with sinuses, or something else. In the same manner, if anxiety is a symptom, it must be symptomatic of some problematic process and not a disorder in itself. In light of this insight, ACT focuses on the processes that turn normal anxious feelings into greatly distressing things such as anxiety disorders and targets those processes rather than the anxious feelings and thoughts per se.

Eifert and Forsyth's (2005) third point of contrast between the two therapies is that whereas CBT sees distinctive approaches as necessary for each particular anxiety disorder, ACT takes into account the recent evidence that points to important shared aspects of ostensibly different anxiety disorders. For example, Barlow, Allen, and Choate (2004) find core features common to all anxiety disorders, meaning that even CBT therapists are starting to see similarities in the treatments for the spectrum of anxiety. Acceptance and commitment therapy, though, has done so all along. Lastly, I noted above that CBT approaches endeavor to conquer anxiety through mastery and control; ACT sees this as not only unnecessary, but possibly even harmful. In all of this, though, Eifert and Forsyth stress that their ACT approach retains parts of CBT (specifically including exposure exercises and addressing escape and avoidance behavior) while focusing more on building better life situations than merely relieving symptoms.

While ACT is useful across the spectrum of anxiety disorders, it de-emphasizes diagnoses (Hayes, Strosahl, & Wilson, 2011). Rather, it points to the common processes that lead to anxiety. A central process is that of experiential avoidance, which is the effortful circumvention of uncomfortable, anxious feelings and related thoughts or imagery. This matches nicely the notion of escape and avoidance behaviors described earlier, and it opens the door to using exposure not only for the feared things, but also for anxiety and anxious feelings themselves. This approach broadens the use of ET even to generalized anxiety disorder (Roemer, Orsillo, & Salters-Pedneault, 2008), where the feelings of the "what ifs" of worry may diminish if the person learns not to avoid the experience of feeling them.

Most importantly, ACT works. Both Hayes et al. (2011) and Batten (2011) list studies that have shown ACT to be effective in treating psychological problems, including anxiety. Hayes et al. in particular note that the theory as a whole and in its parts, not just its treatment application, has empirical support. Even a staunch advocate of CBT like Antony (2011) finds merit in the approach, though he cautions that further research is needed to see how it differs from more established approaches such as CBT, especially as there is notable overlap in many of the concepts. However, Eifert and Forsyth (2005) note work in their own labs finding that ACT-enhanced CBT approaches reduce dropout, especially in the area of exposure, compared to typical CBT. They suggest a vital reason for this is its stated purpose of going beyond just getting rid of anxiety and instead promoting the pursuit of greater life goals without necessarily changing or eliminating anxious feelings.

If ACT provides an approach that overcomes major obstacles to exposure therapies, improves on CBT's treatment for anxiety, and helps reduce experiential avoidance, then it is most appropriate that we consider what it is and particularly how exposure and response prevention play roles in it. To do so, I will summarize ACT as an approach, examine particularly how it is applied to anxiety, explore how exposure is adapted in ACT, and conclude with a look at how ACT-related concepts can be incorporated into more traditional approaches to ET.

An Overview of ACT

Summarizing ACT is a challenge, for as Hayes (2005) makes clear, it is not just a therapeutic package, but an entire model of human functioning and change. While there is a set of techniques associated with it, research on the model encompasses everything from basic processes to the nature of pathology to change process to therapeutic outcome. I will draw much from the latest edition of the foundational work on ACT by Hayes et al. (2011) and refer the interested reader there for a much more detailed summary of ACT, or to Batten (2011) for a helpful if more cursory introduction. I will briefly review some of the theoretical underpinnings and then summarize the basics of the treatment approach.

Underpinnings of ACT

As we observed, ACT is far more than just a set of therapy techniques. It is built on a firm foundation of theory, two central components of which—functional contextualism and relational frame theory (RFT)—I will briefly introduce here.

FUNCTIONAL CONTEXTUALISM

Functional contextualism is the philosophy of science upon which ACT is built, contrasting with most approaches, including CBT (Hayes et al., 2011). Whereas CBT may encourage debate of the logic and reality of certain thoughts, ACT looks instead at the act-in-context, where a thought is situated—a holistic and pragmatic conceptualization that considers the individual act as a whole event occurring in a specific context. "Truth" does not focus on an objective standard, but is a way of assessing how well a behavior functions to achieve a goal. So rather than ask if a behavior (which in ACT can be overt behavior, cognition, or emotion) is logical or true, in ACT one asks if it "works." As the authors suggest, if you are going to the store, the nature of the act is determined only by whether or not you get there, not exactly what you did to get there and if it was the "right" way. It is less concerned with what "ought" to be and more with whether the client is achieving valued goals that are self-determined.

Acceptance and commitment therapy thus points away from the logic or efficiency of behavior and instead considers its purpose. Therapists using ACT often will clarify client statements with questions such as "And that is in the service of ...?" (Hayes et al., 2011, p. 32). Issues of truth and ontology are valid in other ways, but those are beyond the scope of therapy. In practice, this means that counselors perform a functional analysis of behaviors (recall the broad definition here) and how those behaviors help or hinder pursuit of the individual's goals. This specifically includes considering how thoughts and feelings impact other actions and thus promote or deter movement toward goals. For example, a person who avoids crowds due to social anxiety may undermine a valued goal of broadening and improving relationships. In this example one can begin to see how ET has a place in ACT.

RELATIONAL FRAME THEORY

The importance of language and cognition does not go underappreciated in ACT (Hayes et al., 2011). Relational frame theory (RFT) builds on functional contextualism by applying it to human language and cognition. This is a theory that has been very actively studied in the behavior analysis literature over the past decade and explicated nicely in book-length discussions by Hayes, Barnes-Holmes, and Roche (2001) and Törneke (2010). I will look at the most basic aspects of this complex theory as it relates to anxiety in particular.

If a person learns a relationship among several stimuli, she quickly can derive other relations among the class of objects that were not directly learned, forming what is called a *stimulus equivalence class*. This is particularly true of verbal stimuli, because humans can easily form relations between words and other things. Imagine a young person learns that the letters C-A-T apply to the animal of that name. She is later scratched by a cat and then runs away crying. Later, her father might say the word "cat," and the child might cry and run. This is important in anxiety because the sound of the word "cat" can now produce the fear response formerly learned from experience, even in a context where there is no cat present. The sound of the word "cat" is thus derived from the earlier associations, making the set a relational frame. Forming these relational sets can produce emotional responses even when the feared item or situation is not evident.

Such derived relations can evolve to be under tighter contextual control, meaning that certain aspects of the relationships are more likely to occur. In the cat illustration above, a variety of contexts may become associated with "cat" and lead to more frequent fear responses. In some ways, then, this is an improvement on two-factor theory in terms of explaining how a phobia might develop. So hearing the word "cat" may become what is termed the relational context for fear, and this is difficult to unlearn by cognitive means—which is often the goal of CBT.

In contrast, the functional context concerns the impact of such relational responding and is more easily altered; the functional context is therefore a common target in ACT. While there is a time and place for addressing relational contexts, the idea of doing so is to solve problems caused by these relationships. However, ACT often addresses the need for increasing the flexibility of functional contexts. That is, whereas it is unlikely that our little girl who is afraid of cats will unlearn the associations noted, she may learn to have the associations function in different ways so that she is not so inclined to run when she experiences fear. Thus, ACT will focus more on new learning and not on unlearning, something it sees as very difficult to accomplish. Exposure therapy thus can serve to develop new functional contexts for the association of the word "cat" and being afraid, so that functional contexts for the associations are expanded, building the core virtue of ACT: psychological flexibility.

This is a cursory introduction to RFT; readers seeking more information might consult the website of the Association for Contextual Behavioral Science (relationalframetheory.com), though hopefully how these theoretical foundations impact therapy will become more apparent as we consider the ACT model for psychological functioning itself: the *hexaflex*.

The Psychological Flexibility Model

Based on extensive research, ACT proposes *psychological flexibility* as the quality that enables a worthwhile life (Hayes et al., 2011). Six core processes yield psychological flexibility, and problems in these areas create psychological inflexibility; these are illustrated in Figure 7.1. All six interact with each other, with their intersection, if properly aligned, constituting psychological flexibility. A schematic portrayal of this forms the characteristic diagram called a "hexaflex" (Hayes et al., 2011). With all of these processes being common to all people (Batten, 2011), counselor and client are on the same level in coping with life, a key aspect of the ACT therapeutic stance. While Hayes et al. (2011) elaborate on relationships among the six, for the sake of our survey we will simply consider each of these six processes, and their negations, in the context of three healthy response styles: open, centered, and engaged.

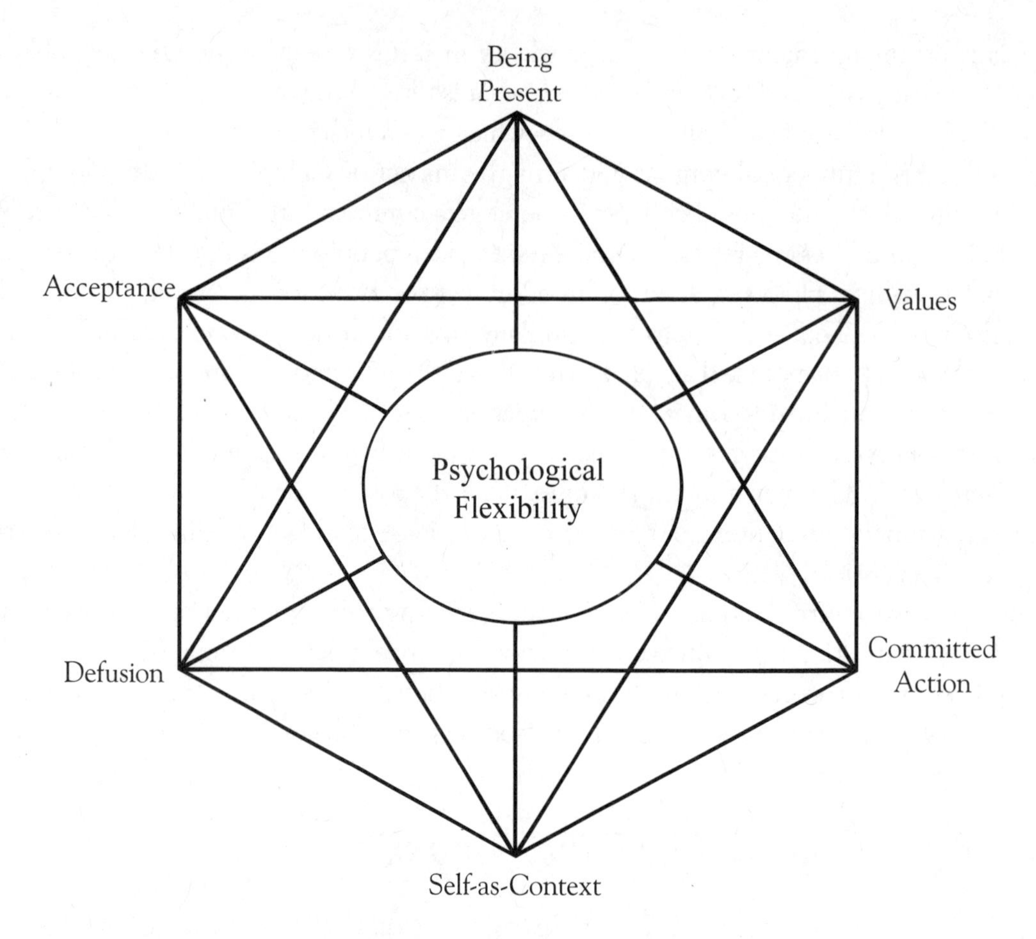

Figure 7.1 Core Processes Yielding Psychological Flexibility

THE OPEN RESPONSE STYLE

Pivotal in ACT is openness to direct experience (Hayes et al., 2011). This openness is hindered when some of the verbal processes described above develop into troublesome associations. Rather than expend energy attempting to control thoughts and experiences, the ACT therapist moves clients toward willingness to experience all of their life events, including "thoughts, feelings, memories and other private events" (Batten, 2011, p. 18).

The first process that supports psychological flexibility is *defusion.* This may best be understood by first considering cognitive fusion, its opposite, which Hayes et al. (2011, p. 69) define as "a process by which verbal events exert strong stimulus control over responding, to the exclusion of other contextual variables." In a sense, verbal events "bully" other aspects of experience, with our associations to words gaining dominance over other experience. For example, our child who learned to fear cats would be fused to the relation of cat/scratching/danger and not open to the pleasant experience of petting a cat and enjoying the sound of its purring. For her, now the thought of a cat, the sound of the word "cat," or the presence of a feline can stimulate the fear. She is fused to the associations of cat and danger and thus avoids any situations that might stimulate these relations.

Defusion, then, is the therapeutic task of building cognitive flexibility and thus undermining the contexts that support and maintain the thought-action relations (Hayes et al., 2011). This is accomplished by helping clients pay attention to the ways they fuse with these thoughts and organize their worlds while helping them build new associations that separate the verbal idea from other things that create anxiety. Here is where a form of exposure can come into play: not passive exposure to the feared object, but exposure in the context of building new associations. For example, the child's therapist might help her play with the sounds in the word "cat" and in so doing gain some cognitive distance from the fearful associations. Thus, the client grows in flexibility in the associations with the verbal stimulus.

The second process is *acceptance* (Hayes et al., 2011). Again, we begin with a consideration of the opposite, in this case experiential avoidance. Experiential avoidance is an unwillingness

> to remain in contact with particular private experiences (e.g., bodily sensations, emotions, thoughts, memories, behavioral predispositions) and [the person] takes steps to alter the form, frequency, or situational sensitivity to these experiences even though doing so is not immediately necessary. (Hayes et al., 2011, p. 73)

Experiential avoidance is much like the avoidance and escape behaviors discussed earlier, with the difference that it is seen as avoidance not merely of fear, but of the full gamut of private experiences. The child who is afraid of cats would thus avoid the experience of being near a cat, avoiding the negative thoughts and feelings, but at the cost of perpetuating them and missing out on the pleasures of petting a cat.

"Acceptance" as used in ACT refers to behavioral willingness and psychological acceptance. It is rooted in the client's willingness, for the sake of his or her values, to make or maintain contact with distressing private experiences or events that may occasion them. It is accomplished by learning to live in the moment and experience what is in that moment as it happens, this being facilitated by mindfulness skills. For the purposes of our current study, this is willingness to expose oneself to the troublesome experience. Yet, unlike simple behavioral exposure, this is done with a focus on mindfulness and in the service of valued goals. We will return to this shortly, as this is the key place where ET melds into ACT.

THE CENTERED RESPONSE STYLE

The openness in response just described by defusion and acceptance, and the engagement of the two (described in the following section), are actions taken in particular contexts. Therapy, however, most often begins with the centering of therapist and client in the present moment, with psychological flexibility being the ability to move among these three positions as need be (Hayes et al., 2011). The two core processes of the hexaflex here, falling in the middle of the diagram, are flexible attention to the present moment and self-as-context (see Figure 7.1). While these are vital elements of the ACT model, we will review them more briefly as they are less directly related to exposure therapy.

Flexible attention to the present moment is a most basic process, as one must be psychologically present at any given moment in order to respond to the context of the contingencies that present in that moment. Hayes et al. (2011) wisely observe that the present is the only time when anything happens. This is a vital point for persons with unwanted anxiety, for anxiety largely consists of unwelcome feelings due to cognitively being "present" in the past or future, not the present. The "what ifs" so common to worry and anxiety keep the individual feeling the fear of a future consequence, compromising awareness of the current moment and thus compromising the quality of life. We have already seen that CBT has added mindfulness elements, and these are also important in DBT, but it is good to be reminded how important these are for treating anxiety. Exposure especially encourages experience in the present moment.

Self-as-context is also known as *the observing self* (Batten, 2011) and is a requisite for being fully present in the moment. People develop a "self as content" in that they form self-conceptualizations of who they are, which may be threatened by events or ideas that contradict these. Holding too tightly to such self-conceptualizations creates psychological inflexibility and thus hampers openness to experience. A person might conclude that he is a fearful person, or simply shy, and use this to brush off experiences that might afford the opportunity to learn that he is not a fearful person but merely a person who has fears *and* perhaps also a number of life goals that have little to do with those fears.

Psychological flexibility is reached by seeing the self as a context for experience, a place of perspective. It is the positioning of the self in a place that transcends the moment-to-moment content of subjective experience. Verbal events (such as anxious thoughts) can be seen from a more transcendent perspective, something often provided by an individual's spirituality. As a person steps outside himself (so to speak), he can better see the moment and is better equipped to disentangle himself from his anxious thinking. Consider a woman who is frightened by a scary film, but is able to mentally step back and see herself as a context in that she is merely watching images projected onto a screen.

THE ENGAGED RESPONSE STYLE

Life is more than the mere absence of pathology, a point lost in many therapies that focus exclusively on getting rid of unpleasant symptoms. A return to "neutral" may be seen as adequate, without keeping the patient's broader life in view. In ACT, psychological flexibility enables a person to live in the present moment, but with the purpose of connecting with personal values. While ACT does not purport to dictate any particular values, it *does* maintain that life is concerned with working in conjunction with values in the real world. A cost of anxiety is how it prevents people from engaging in activities consistent with their values. For example, take the girl who fears cats. A value might be cultivating friendships, but if her friend has a cat in the house, the fear could derail her from going to her friend's house in service of the value of relationship. Inappropriate anxiety does not merely yield unpleasantnesses, but cheats the person out of valued goods. Individuals then need to engage with values through committed actions.

Values in ACT are freely chosen, verbally constructed, ongoing patterns of activity that are intrinsically reinforcing (Hayes et al., 2011); these are not to be confused with values as what a person sees as right or wrong morally. Note the behavioral terminology in this: what one values impacts what is reinforcing. Doing and pursuing what one values is naturally rewarding, and likely more so than if one simply adds an external reward. In contrast to this is waiting for things to happen, reacting to others rather than intentionally pursuing one's own values, or overvaluing pleasing others to the denigration of oneself. Clients who learn to move toward valuing may see how anxious avoidance hinders this and thus may be more open to exposure to discomfort as a necessary step toward the thing valued. As in physical conditioning, they understand: no pain, no gain.

Committed action is merely values in action, where acting in consonance with values is a logical consequence of the values held. The contrasting qualities are inaction (the failure to act on values) and impulsivity (reacting to fleeting contexts). Committed action is acting moment by moment in ways that pursue and sustain higher purposes. Actions are directed toward goals that flow from one's values. If one values friendship, then a goal when moving to a new town would be to act so as to meet new people and get to know them. For persons with anxiety, learning more of their values will encourage movement toward those intrinsic reinforcers, even if it may involve accepting some anxious feelings in the process.

Acceptance and commitment therapy, then, "uses acceptance and mindfulness processes and commitment and behavioral activation processes to produce psychological flexibility" (Hayes et al., 2011, p. 97). It is not so much about symptom reduction as developing the skills to adapt flexibly to life and pursue one's goals. As for anxiety, it is a form of psychological inflexibility that undermines the ability to live a value-based life. It is likely that movement toward flexibility will reduce anxious symptoms, but that is incidental. More so, the idea is to accept anxiety as part of life so that the pain of anxiety does not become the suffering of a stifled, limited life.

The Place of Exposure Therapy in ACT for Anxiety

Having touched on some of the applications of ACT to the treatment of persons with anxiety, I now focus on these therapeutic strategies, and in particular how these relate to exposure therapy. For readers seeking a more comprehensive description of using ACT with anxiety, Eifert and Forsyth (2005) offer an excellent text that includes a number of useful handouts and forms. The authors followed this with a superb workbook for clients (Forsyth & Eifert, 2007), which offers lay-level explanations of the ideas of ACT and exercises to aid in skill development to grow through anxiety.

Acceptance and commitment therapists make clear that a therapist who models psychological flexibility, the therapeutic relationship, and a good functional assessment are all prerequisites for effective therapy (Hayes, et al., 2011; Eifert & Forsyth, 2005). Those resources provide details on these important aspects of ACT; I will present a simplified summary of a course of ACT with focus on the use of exposure.

From Control to Willingness

Most anxious clients enter therapy disheartened, as their efforts to control their anxieties have failed. Indeed, often anxiety itself exists as an effort to control future outcomes and avoid negative events or feelings. Stated differently, anxious clients have historically refused to accept anxious feelings and have utilized escape and avoidance strategies in a futile effort to control their experience. However, "a core principle of the ACT approach is that attempts at controlling and eliminating unwanted private experiences are driven by cultural rules that specify health as freedom from unwanted and distressing private experiences" (Hayes et al., 2011, p. 180). Acceptance and commitment therapy sees a certain level of pain as an inevitable, essential part of life. When one fights against this pain, normal pain turns into unnecessary suffering. To be ready for change, the client must be aided to see that all of her control efforts have failed and that it is time for a new effort (Eifert & Forsyth, 2005). The therapist promotes what ACT calls "creative hopelessness" (Hayes et al., 2011), as exercises and discussion move the individual to the point of awareness of the failure of her control strategies. In the course of so doing, the client may even learn how efforts to control actually worsen anxiety.

Part of trying to control anxiety involves escaping from places where it occurs or avoiding them altogether. This strategy keeps the person ever alert to contexts where the feared thought or situation might appear and thus makes him anxious to avoid the anxiety. Even with a degree of success in avoiding the actual feared object, the fear of fear becomes the problem more than the feared object itself. While control can work for some things, anxiety is rarely one of them.

This insight is pivotal in relation to ET and RP. Response prevention is targeted at the escape and avoidance behaviors and serves to prevent them in some way, forcing "exposure." While parents might be able to implement such a plan with children by controlling contingencies for these behaviors, it often will not work well with adults who must control their own contingencies. In relation to ACT in general, RP is a poor fit, as it merely strives to limit maladaptive behaviors without a greater focus on committed action to values.

Once the therapist succeeds in moving the client to see the hopelessness of control, she must move to where the client is willing to accept discomfort. This is the point at which the therapist needs to introduce a focus on the client's values. It is through the focus on values, and the behaviors that are necessary to move in their direction, that the client may start to become willing to accept the discomfort of anxiety. In other words, exposure is not done to conquer or reduce anxiety through mere willpower, but it occurs as a natural by-product of the client's moving toward her chosen values. This is why ACT therapists always pose the question of whether a person is willing to experience anxiety in the context of values: Are you willing to experience the pain of anxiety if it means moving toward and getting closer to your chosen values?

From Avoidance to Acceptance

Eifert and Forsyth (2005) restate the acronym ACT to mean Accepting thoughts and feelings, Choosing direction, and Taking actions, a catchy summary of the treatment goals. The first goal is to move from avoiding personal experience of unwanted thoughts and feelings to accepting them. The cognitive side of this problem with openness is addressed through defusion techniques, which are beyond the scope of our discussion other than to mention that these cousins of cognitive interventions may facilitate exposure to feared stimuli and even are a form of exposure in themselves, as they invite the client to expose himself to the fusion of relations that causes anxiety as he learns ways of distancing himself through defusion—often in the context of humor. This is what happens when the child who fears cats is encouraged to verbally play with the word "cat" itself. It defuses, but also is a form of exposure in that she keeps a fear-evoking word in mind without avoiding it. Progress in learning to defuse also paves the way for in vivo exposure as part of moving toward chosen values.

The idea of acceptance, then, is to turn unneeded suffering into ordinary pain (Eifert & Forsyth, 2005); these authors use "suffering" to refer to the pain caused by experiential avoidance. More specifically, they use "active acceptance" to refer to letting go of the struggle with thoughts and feelings they cannot control. One then mindfully acknowledges these feelings without seeing them as absolute facts that require action, the mindfulness helping to distance the thought or feeling from its almost automatic (fused) interpretation. As Eifert and Forsyth note, the goal in ACT is to *feel* better rather than feel *better* (that is, to mindfully attend to feelings as they are and thus feel them better, rather than rid oneself of the feelings to improve one's feeling state, which is to feel less). Here is exposure in ACT: the willingness to be with anxious thoughts and feelings without attempting to fight or flee, with the purpose of pursuing chosen life goals. Again, the sources mentioned above provide very helpful exercises to help develop these skills.

We see that exposure in ACT is not simply about facing the fear, or facing it while distracting oneself somehow, but about *accepting* the thoughts and feelings to which one is exposed so that they become no longer an impediment to valued action. This is a vital difference and one that enhances the traditional use of ET.

From Reaction to Choice

Eifert and Forsyth's (2005) second step in their reworking of the ACT acronym is for the client to choose directions. Anxious clients often move in only one direction: away—away from fear, thoughts of fears, or situations that evoke fear. Like a pinball, they move in reaction to events as they unfold. If one is anxious, she is more apt to live life avoiding than approaching. There is little purpose or direction other than to escape pain, which, as we have seen, merely leads to more suffering.

Instead, ACT teaches skills to enable the person to clarify valued goals at which to aim. Unlike a pinball, a bullet well aimed will move through obstacles as it heads undeterred to its target. Of course, one must identify the target first, which is why ACT works with clients to uncover values that have been neglected and have suffered in the clients' manic efforts to avoid the experience of anxiety. Once values are chosen and clarified, committed action toward them is possible. Anxious thoughts and feelings are likely to be obstacles, but with willingness, they will not be avoided anymore. A vital contribution of ACT is that it adds more motivation (the pursuit of one's values) to expose oneself to anxious situations.

Regaining "Control" in Committed Action

The ACT client regains a sense of control in his ability to take action deliberately to pursue valued goals. This is not "control" in the sense of controlling feelings of anxiety. This is the path of the "bullet," the way to achieve the goal of living out one's values undaunted by the normal pain and anxious feelings that may come.

Eifert and Forsyth (2005, p. 200) make clear that "exposure within ACT is always done in the service of a client's valued life goals." It is an extension of mindfulness; mindfulness skills will serve the client well during exposure trials. Since they view traditional exposure as having some negative associations, Eifert and Forsyth call the exercises FEEL: Feeling Experiences Enhances Living. The client is asked to endure discomfort not for the meager sake of symptom reduction, but with an eye to a full and meaningful life. Experiential avoidance hinders this full life, and the focus on a chosen goal gives the discomfort meaning. In short, "in ACT the goal [of exposure] is psychological flexibility in pursuit of committed action" (Hayes et al., 2011, p. 339).

Moreover, Hayes et al. (2011) note that exposure can also serve as a means of learning acceptance because it is an exercise in staying in the moment in the midst of distress, while practicing defusion when experiencing anxious feelings. Finally, they note that each exposure activity is in itself an act of commitment, as it facilitates living more in accord with one's values.

Exposure, then, is put into a powerful context in ACT, which puts it in service of higher goals; ACT also equips the client with mindfulness and acceptance skills that help her stay in the moment when anxious feelings arise. While the place and goal of exposure in ACT differs from its place and goals in established cognitive and behavioral therapies, there are some procedural similarities, such as the use of graded exposure—moving from imaginal to in vivo or even interoceptive exposures.

The Place of ACT in Exposure Therapy

A practitioner of more traditional CBT may be daunted by the complexity and differences of ACT and hesitant to make the paradigm shift to become an ACT therapist. In closing this discussion, I'll give brief note to some work that demonstrates that some ACT concepts and strategies can be cut and pasted into more traditional exposure therapies. Observing some of the advantages of ACT, Orsillo, Roemer, and Holowka (2005) comment that

> acceptance based approaches may enhance the effect of exposure therapy by directly addressing existing concerns about clients' unwillingness to engage in exposure, the complexities of exposure with comorbid conditions, and the reduced utility of this approach with highly avoidant clients. (p. 25)

In so stating, they argue that the concepts of acceptance and mindfulness can be productively used to enhance traditional CBT; members of this authorial team went on to develop what they call acceptance-based behavior therapy (ABBT; Roemer et al., 2008).

While some aspects of the control focus of CBT, especially in regard to cognitions themselves, conflict with the ACT theory we have reviewed, two aspects of ACT are rather readily imported into traditional ET. First, it may well be helpful to use mindfulness techniques to enhance acceptance of feelings and thoughts during exposure exercises rather than forcing the client to just tolerate them or, worse, distract himself from them. Second, contextualizing exposure in the service of higher personal goals, or values, can be accomplished without utilizing the entire ACT model. Making these relatively simple adaptations to basic exposure therapy may help solve the major issues of treatment compliance and even dropout.

These supplements to more traditional ET might be better understood through an illustration. Recall Melanie and how she was so afraid of having a wreck that she began avoiding driving and was even fearful if someone else was at the wheel. If we assume that her fear was simply too overwhelming for her to execute the exposures in a CBT context, even with some relaxation strategies and coping cognitions, elements of ACT might be introduced.

Melanie's therapist, Dr. Smith, might help Melanie reevaluate a mastery and control framework and use ACT techniques to help Melanie reach a creative hopelessness about "beating" anxiety and move toward a mindful acceptance of the anxious feelings associated with driving, accepting them with willingness rather than fighting them. Exposure is a way to put these acceptance skills into play in Melanie's real life. Therapy could also shift goals; rather than moving from problematic anxiety to "normal," the goal becomes helping Melanie grasp the values in her life, see how her anxiety keeps her from pursuing these values, and move through the anxiety in pursuit of them. For example, she might value achieving a sense of accomplishment through a promotion at work into the job she actually trained for. Her inability to get to meetings in other parts of town has hindered her job performance. Her commitment to pursuing this promotion gives her further reason to accept the anxiety of driving or riding as she wills herself to go to these meetings. Thus, vital concepts of ACT afford a fresh approach to the feelings (acceptance versus mastery) and new rationale for exposures (committed action versus trying to be normal).

Acceptance and commitment therapy is a refreshing, comprehensive, and evidence-based approach to anxiety that moves beyond a focus on symptom reduction to building a life lived fully in the context of values and related goals. It quite naturally incorporates exposure into its program and appears to be a valid approach for the spectrum of anxiety disorders. The only cases where I might have some reservations regarding its use are those of relatively simple phobias or mild anxieties where clients are not as resistant to traditional exposure and so may be treated in a shorter time than ACT might require.

Clearly the positive goals in ACT are attractive, but the clinician must judge when a problem can be resolved with less effort, especially in a world of managed care, which may opt for the simplest solution to the presenting problem rather than one that takes more time (and thus money) to make a better life for the client. Of course, ACT therapists are not as concerned with diagnosis (Hayes et al., 2011) as many other therapists. While that is quite commendable, many counselors are limited by the demands of the system of payment and may not have the liberty to use ACT as much as they would like when problems are simpler and quicker resolutions are possible with basic ET or short-term CBT.

That said, ACT is quite promising, and hopefully this skimming of the surface will tempt you to dig deeper into this rich and enticing therapy.

Chapter 8

Three Other Adaptations of Exposure Therapy

In the preceding three chapters we saw that exposure therapy is an ingredient that can be incorporated into a variety of therapeutic models, including CBT, DBT, and ACT. All of that is over and above its utility as a purely behavioral treatment, discussed in Chapter 4. In this chapter I will give shorter treatment to three other important adaptions of exposure therapy.

We begin with prolonged exposure therapy (PE), which introduces us to the important notion of emotional processing in the exposure process and how it can be used to help those suffering from post-traumatic stress disorder (PTSD) in particular. Next is narrative exposure therapy (NET), a very promising adaptation that is proving useful and effective in areas torn by war and other trauma. Prolonged exposure in particular opens the door to moving exposure therapy beyond the anxiety disorders to help people deal with other affective unpleasantnesses, as we'll see in the third model we'll review, emotional exposure (EE).

Prolonged Exposure Therapy

In considering this variant of exposure therapy built largely on the work of Foa and her colleagues (for example, Foa et al., 2007), we will note the underlying theory, consider its relevance to the primary target of PTSD, and survey the model of treatment built on it.

Emotional Processing Theory

Prolonged exposure therapy (PE) traces its roots to the seminal article of Foa and Kozak (1986) on the emotional processing of fear and how exposure can serve as corrective information to that process. Their emotional processing theory begins with the notion of *fear structures* existing in memory, these being programs that are used to escape danger, that involve physiological arousal, and that are not completely available to the conscious mind. These fear structures include data about the feared stimulus; information concerning responses, be they verbal, physiological, or behavioral; and a model of interpreting the stimulus and responding to it. A fear structure is activated when threat is perceived, and it serves as a blueprint of what one is to do when afraid, which is basically to avoid or escape the feared stimulus. Given that, fear activation must be preceded by physiological changes that prepare the person for action.

Fear structures can be modified through emotional processing, which has two basic requirements: fear-relevant stimuli must be encountered in such a way as to activate the fear memory in the fear structure; and once activated the memory must encounter information that is incompatible with the memory and thus produce a new memory. This change is termed *emotional processing.* Foa and Kozak (1986) found that patients who did well in exposure therapy showed both elements: an activation of fear during exposure and a gradual decrease in fear (or habituation) over the course of the exposure. A third element of emotional processing becomes evident over time as in subsequent sessions the initial arousal to the feared stimulus declines (across-session habituation). All three are needed for emotional processing to occur, and thus a model of how effective exposure therapy should be conducted is implied.

The nature of the exposure must be such as to adequately activate the fear response, whether it be an imaginal or in vivo exposure; it is unclear which in general is superior. Also, Foa and Kozak (1986) report that measures of fear (for example, heart rate or skin conductance) follow a fairly regular pattern of escalating, plateauing, and then decreasing. This pattern needs to be allowed to run its full course to maximize emotional processing. Foa and Kozak cite literature that shows that during exposures, anxiety only begins to decrease after about fifty minutes, so a session that allows an exposure to continue until anxiety abates will need to last closer to ninety minutes. Regarding the common question of whether or not the client should attend to her anxious feelings and thoughts or distract herself during exposure, they found that maintaining attention to the feared stimulus during exposure made little difference within sessions, but facilitated more progress between sessions. These findings form the basic parameters for PE.

Emotional Processing in PTSD

Foa's (2007) PE therapy is specifically designed for persons with PTSD and is built on her particular model for how PTSD develops. This model begins with the trauma creating a specific pathological fear structure (Foa, 2011) that includes inaccurate associations among stimuli and responses that happened to be present at the time of the trauma. This causes the traumatic memory structure to include a large number of stimulus elements that are not genuinely associated with the trauma and thus gives more frequent occasion for the memory structure to be activated. For instance, if a woman who was sexually assaulted makes the association "any man might rape me," then encountering any man might trigger the memory. A second feature of trauma (Foa, 2011) may include the individual concluding that he did not handle the trauma well and thus feel unable to cope and incompetent. Both of these elements put the individual at risk for increasing avoidance of any thoughts or cues of the trauma as they trigger these misperceptions and the concomitant anxiety and distress.

Foa and Cahill (2001) argued that for many (or most) victims of trauma, daily life provides a series of natural exposures that promote emotional processing to resolve the fearful memories to a tolerable degree. These individuals would naturally encounter things that would activate the trauma memory and its relevant thoughts and feelings; this includes talking about the event(s) to friends and loved ones. These experiences then disconfirm the memory (Foa et al., 2007) and the individual can relearn that the world is basically a safe place and that she is competent after all. Of course, repeated trauma will complicate this process.

However, if the individual takes a course of avoiding any trauma-related thoughts, situations, or images (Foa, 2011), emotional processing does not take place and recovery from the trauma is inhibited. This excessive avoidance of trauma reminders can result in the development of chronic PTSD (Foa et al., 2007), the initial trauma being exacerbated by the pattern of negative reinforcement whereby the avoidance (be it in one's environment or just one's mind) instantly eases anxiety, increasing the likelihood of using avoidance again in the future. It logically follows from this theory that treatment would be to create the conditions for emotional processing that did not occur naturally.

Prolonged Exposure for PTSD

In the model just presented, PTSD is maintained by avoiding the emotional processing needed to disconfirm fear structures that overestimate danger in the environment and incompetence in the individual. The goal of PE, then, is to promote emotional processing via systematically confronting stimuli associated with the trauma (Foa, 2011). It incorporates both imaginal exposure in session and in vivo exposure between sessions (with this experience being discussed in the following session). The objective in both is to activate the fear memory and to disconfirm the expectations of disaster the person may have.

A central aspect of the imaginal exposure in session is recounting in detail the most upsetting memory from the trauma, to allow the individual to reorganize the memory, reconsider her negative perceptions about her conduct during the trauma (that is, that she was incompetent), and learn to distinguish between thinking about the trauma and reexperiencing the trauma; to allow habituation to the traumatic memory to occur; and to demonstrate that no harm comes by thinking about the trauma. The central point is that the person activates the traumatic memory and then allows the resulting anxiety to resolve naturally (without escape or avoidance). Once the imaginal exposure (which lasts up to an hour or so) is concluded, therapist and client process the experience to show contradictions between the client's perceptions and what was actually recalled during the exposure.

Treatment is surprisingly brief at eight to fifteen sessions of sixty to ninety minutes apiece (Foa, 2011). Very specific guidance on the step-by-step implementation of the process is found in Foa et al. (2007), and their accompanying workbook (Rothbaum, Foa, & Hembree, 2007) is helpful for clients (there is also a workbook specifically for adolescents [Chrestman, Gilboa-Schechtman, & Foa, 2008]). Prolonged exposure has received considerable empirical support for its efficacy with PTSD and has the most support of any exposure therapy for that disorder (Foa, 2011). It has been used effectively with different types of trauma, including combat-related PTSD (Yoder et al., 2011). Research cited by Foa (2011) has also shown that ET can be used by community therapists and is well tolerated by patients, undergirding Foa's pacesetting work of disseminating this treatment in a variety of ways.

While it is beyond the purview of our discussion to examine medication for anxiety spectrum disorders, it is interesting to note that Foa (2011) suggests one future direction for exposure therapy for PTSD is the use of pharmacological agents to enhance inhibitory learning during exposure. While there is apparently no data regarding its use in PTSD yet, D-cycloserine has been shown to enhance the efficacy of exposure therapy if administered just before and after exposures (see Norberg, Krystal, & Tolin, 2008, for a meta-analysis). This may offer promise to many persons with anxiety as research progresses on this idea.

The notion of emotional processing and its relation to exposure has been adapted in several ways beyond Foa's model. We will see how emotional processing is used in narrative exposure therapy and then turn our attention to the implications of emotional exposure beyond the anxiety spectrum.

Narrative Exposure Therapy

Trauma can be divided into at least two types (Herman, 1992). One can be traumatized by a single, tragic event such as being raped or witnessing a fatal car crash (Type I traumatic event). As we just saw, failure to emotionally process such an event can lead to PTSD. But what if a person experiences prolonged or repeated trauma (Type II events)? This is termed "complex trauma" and is the regrettable fate of many individuals in areas of war, terror, and torture (Schauer et al., 2005), and of individuals with repeated traumas such as being sexually molested over a period of time. It is marked by dysregulation of affect and impulses, alteration in consciousness and attention, somatization of the stress, and alterations in self-perception, the perception of others, and one's system of meaning.

To address complex trauma after war, terror, or torture, Schauer et al. (2005) developed a model known as narrative exposure therapy (NET). Their 2005 book offers a summary of the model and its effectiveness, which has been remarkable. Most of the research on the model has been conducted outside of the Americas, in areas torn by war and strife. Narrative exposure therapy has been shown to be effective with African refugees in settlements (Neuner, Schauer, Klaschik, Karunakara, & Elbert, 2004), with asylum seekers (Neuner, et al., 2010), and with children and adolescents (Ruf et al., 2010). It has even been successfully utilized in the field by lay counselors (Neuner et al., 2008). As psychotherapy broadens out of the Western context, it is important to see how exposure is flexible enough to be adapted across cultures and to benefit those who have experienced horrific trauma.

Basic Theory of NET

Narrative exposure therapy (Schauer et al., 2005) stresses two core elements in complex trauma: the role of memory and the processing of affective experience. Memory is a central issue in PTSD, as made evident by symptoms such as flashbacks of the traumatic events. The sensory elements of the trauma are particularly strong in memory yet the person may be unable to translate this into communicable language. While details and affective representations abound in the mind of the person with trauma, he or she generally lacks an adequately coherent structure of the memory to make sense of it and successfully emotionally process it. This disorganization of memory is posited as the source of the core symptoms of PTSD.

This is the result of traumatic memories being stored in the brain differently than typical memories. They include very vivid sensory perceptual representations of the events, and these are stored in *fear structures*, borrowing from the seminal work of Foa and Kozak (1986) discussed above. These are particularly large memory structures with quite powerful connections between single elements, such as the sight and sound associated with the trauma, as they were stored in memory while the person was highly aroused emotionally. This accounts for the phenomenon of flashbacks, as these sensory cues to the event are encoded with great emotional connotation. This conceptualization also nicely accounts for the frequent avoidance seen in those with PTSD, who understandably endeavor to detour around anything that can evoke these memories.

In contrast, most of our memories of past events are autobiographical (Schauer et al., 2005) and marked by general representations of periods of our lives, such as "when I was living in the dorm." These are then organized into general events (patterns of life such as playing in the yard) or specific events (one's wedding day) and finally into things specific to individual events. This type of memory is quite disjointed in those with PTSD so that the period of trauma has emotional and event cues (*hot memory*) and pieces of information, but lacks the coherent organization and recollection of normal autobiography (*cool memory*). This leaves the person with highly charged fear structures yet lacking a coherent narrative of the events of the trauma.

The lack of clearly organized autobiographical memory renders emotional processing of the trauma exceedingly difficult and leaves the person highly conditioned to respond to fear. In the NET model (Schauer et al., 2005), simply exposing individuals to the fear triggers will not be adequate to eliminate fear responses. Rather, emotional processing must include the reconstruction of the autobiographical memory of the event. This builds more cool-memory context for the activation of the affective memories. This is a challenging process of exposure to the emotional and autobiographical aspects of the time of trauma, but it facilitates making a chronology of the traumatic period and enables the person to separate past threats from the present.

The NET Approach to Complex Trauma

Schauer et al. (2005) build on Foa's (Foa et al., 2007) model of exposure therapy for PTSD and add a component of developing autobiographical accounts of the trauma to promote the needed change in fear structures described above. The goal of NET is to build a consistent autobiographical representation (or declarative memory) of the sequence of events in the trauma, while in so doing exposing the person to sensory images of the events and allowing for habituation to these. Exposure is thus only part of the model; therapy also reorganizes declarative memories of the events to place them into their proper space and time.

Narrative exposure therapy (Schauer et al., 2005) was developed specifically for the treatment of PTSD consequent to organized violence, and it blends exposure therapy with testimony therapy. The latter means that a single event (for example, being mugged) is not the focus, but rather the development of a narration of one's whole life, including a focus on the period of life in which the trauma occurred. In the process, cool declarative memories elicit hot implicit memories, which the person then habituates to.

ELEMENTS OF NET

Narrative exposure therapy thus has two foci. It uses exposure therapy to reduce PTSD symptoms through habituation. Yet, as Schauer et al. (2005) note, more is necessary: specifically it is important to reconstruct an autobiographical memory out of the distorted pieces in the mind of the victim.

The elements of treatment that Schauer et al. (2005) argue are proven effective include the active chronological reconstruction of the autobiographical memory, prolonged exposure to the "hot spots," and full activation of the fear structure to enable emotional processing and separation of the memory from the current triggers. Physiological and somatosensory responses are linked and integrated in their appropriate past and present contexts. Similar to CBT, NET also sees cognitive reevaluation of one's behavior and cognitions, along with their meanings, as important, as well as regaining one's sense of dignity through developing a testimony in the context of affirming human rights.

PROCEDURES OF NET

To reach these objectives and address the elements just described, NET's overarching technique (Schauer et al., 2005) is for the counselor to guide the individual to develop a narrative that covers his or her entire lifetime, beginning with life prior to the first traumatic event, detailing experiences in order through the period of trauma, including any flight from the trauma (as many who receive NET are refugees), life in the refugee camp or other placement, and hopes and fears about the future.

Given the context in which NET is used, it is a very short-term approach; while length varies, it typically lasts eight to twelve sessions. As therapist and client work together to construct a consistent narrative of the client's biography, the therapist supports the client in mentally reliving events and emotionally processing them. The therapist writes down the testimony of the client and subsequently reads it back to correct it or fill in additional details. The initial session consists of diagnosis and psychoeducation and the second begins the narration, covering from birth until the onset of trauma. Subsequent sessions consist in reviewing the narrative from previous sessions and moving through the rest of the trauma and to the present. In the final session the entire testimony is read and signed.

A vital aspect of NET is that the narrative slows down when addressing the trauma and takes care that the narrative is imbedded in the broader life story, grounding the cues for fear. In the course of therapy the hot memories of sensations and feelings are connected to corresponding memory fragments in the autobiography and put into words, relating them to declarative memory (which is more "factual" and less emotional). The movement of hot memory to cool is roughly the same curve of habituation we saw with PE, with it increasing, peaking, and then declining within a single session.

Thus, exposure, and particularly PE, are effectively adapted for use with those who have suffered almost unimaginable trauma in some of the most tragic settings of the world. Exposure and its variants are impressively flexible. But to this point we have only looked at anxiety spectrum disorders. The future of exposure likely will include increasing use with other emotional distresses.

Emotional Exposure

It is not insignificant that Foa terms the core process in exposure "emotional processing" and not just "fear processing." She notes (Foa, 2011) that a variant of PE has also been found effective with grief and that exposure has been used effectively in depression to target experiential avoidance. If one assumes that pathological emotions result from erroneous perceptions and are maintained through avoidance that cuts off disconfirming experience, then exposure therapies may be effective when other emotions are the focus of treatment. We will trace two treatment models that move exposure therapy out of the realm of anxiety and into use with a broader range of emotions.

Exposure-Based Cognitive Therapy for Depression

Possibly the first person to suggest that exposure principles could be used effectively with other affective disorders was Rachman (1980). However, more recently it has been Adele Hayes (not to be confused with ACT founder Steven Hayes) and her colleagues who have developed this into a model and researched it (Hayes et al., 2005, 2007, and Kumar, Feldman, & Hayes, 2008).

Hayes et al. (2005) observe that emotion regulation is essential to mental health and is thus a concern when pathology is present. We have seen in our discussion of the spectrum of anxiety disorders that those prone to anxiety have difficulty regulating emotion and often resort to experiential avoidance in a (futile) attempt to escape intolerable emotion. When something triggers the anxiety, the result is poorly controlled emotion and a tendency to worry about the situation rather than manage the emotion. Avoidance and rumination easily characterize anxiety and, as we have seen, exposure techniques have proven effective in addressing this cycle.

However, evidence suggests the general process is not very different with depression (Hayes et al., 2005). Those who are depressed have a tendency to ruminate on their negative mood and life circumstances, with this process being easily activated and becoming overwhelming in a pattern very much like anxiety. There is also a tendency then to avoid starting this ruminative process, through experiential avoidance. Finally, as with anxiety, the effort to avoid the affect may rebound to make the dysregulation worse once triggered. This being the case, treatment of depression would need to focus on changing patterns of avoidance and rumination—areas where exposure can help.

The model originated to accomplish this is called exposure-based cognitive therapy for depression (EBCT; Hayes et al., 2007, though the model is more fully detailed in Hayes & Harris, 2000). Citing the destabilization before therapeutic change seen in exposure therapy (Foa & Kozak, 1986), the authors see a similar pattern as needful with depression, as those suffering from it seek to avoid unpleasant emotions and experiences and need to have these to disturb the avoidant patterns and initiate change. Hayes et al. (2007) argue that reducing avoidance and rumination and promoting processing of disturbing emotions are key to treating depression, as with exposure therapy for anxiety. They cite behavioral activation therapy (Dimidjian et al., 2006) and mindfulness-based cognitive therapy (Segal, Williams, & Teasdale, 2002) as forerunners to their approach in using strategies comparable to exposure therapy for anxiety disorders.

Goals for EBCT (Hayes et al., 2007) include fully activating all aspects of the depressive network, increasing the client's ability to tolerate avoided emotions and thoughts, and exposing him to corrective information to facilitate emotional processing. While this has similarities to Foa's (Foa et al., 2007) model as discussed above, it adds more stress to cognitive analysis and meaning-making; the process is thus termed "cognitive-emotional processing." While this is not a pure exposure therapy, it is organized around exposure as the central component. This therapy includes an element of mindfulness training, and the treatment improves mindfulness as it relieves depression (Kumar et al., 2008), with data suggesting that EBCT is an effective treatment (Hayes et al., 2005, 2007).

Typically, EBCT (Kumar et al., 2008) consists of some twenty to twenty-four sessions covering three phases, and it points to a healthier lifestyle, not just the alleviation of depression. The first eight sessions make up phase one, and focus on stress management—teaching problem-solving and coping skills in addition to healthy lifestyle skills and mindfulness. This prepares clients for the second phase (sessions nine through eighteen), which is destabilizing, and invites clients to use their new skills to approach previously avoided material that also, alternately, overwhelms them while they ruminate on it. This is an activation/exposure phase and uses exposure in the service of cognitive-emotion regulation much as Foa et al. (2007) use it for emotional processing. The final phase (sessions nineteen or twenty through twenty-four) consolidates gains and promotes positive growth as the therapist scaffolds the client in seeking a healthier and more purposeful future. Here mindfulness skills are applied to positive emotions and experiences that may have been suppressed while the person was more depressed, all with an eye to avoiding relapse.

While response prevention is not specifically discussed in EBCT, it is easy to see that one must inhibit the reflexive avoidance behaviors, such as physical withdrawal or excessive sleeping, that are evident in depression. Here, again, exposure therapy and response prevention appear to be remarkably effective in and adaptable to a range of therapeutic models.

A Unified Protocol for Transdiagnostic Treatment of Emotional Disorders

The trend to adapt exposure therapy to other emotional disorders includes the work of Barlow (Barlow et al., 2011), who is also known for his landmark work on anxiety disorders (Barlow, 2002). Barlow and colleagues (2011) offer a protocol that can be used across the spectrum of anxiety disorders and the forms of unipolar depression. McKay, Fanning, and Ona (2011) offer a manual for a similar program, describing it as universal rather than unified.

THEORY OF THE MODELS

McKay et al. (2011) draw their methods from three universal treatments for emotional disorders that have a solid research base and are the ones we examined in Chapters 5 through 7: cognitive behavioral therapy, dialectical behavior therapy, and acceptance and commitment therapy. Acknowledging that on which of these is best the jury is still out and likely will be for a while, McKay and colleagues argue that given the effectiveness of all three, core elements of each will also be productive in the lives of clients. They situate pain in seven transdiagnostic factors that are ineffective strategies to cope with emotion in the short run and that over the long haul actually intensify the problem. They offer a workbook to address these that is built around the eight core components of the three models above: values in action, mindfulness and emotional awareness, defusion, cognitive flexibility training, self-soothing, doing the opposite, interpersonal effectiveness, and three types of emotional exposure (imagery-based, interoceptive, and situational). While helpful to therapists, this text is intended primarily for use by clients or lay individuals seeking to help themselves.

While McKay et al. (2011) work from the empirical support of their sources, Barlow et al. (2011) conducted a trial of their model across a wide age range of those with anxiety disorders, with some 73 percent reaching responder status, data comparable to existing CBT protocols. They are continuing their research program around the world.

The unified protocol (UP) of Barlow et al. (2011) is the union of two streams: cognitive behavioral approaches and the findings of emotion science. Regarding the former, UP draws from the cognitive behavioral treatments that have empirical support the principles these hold in common. These include reassessing maladaptive cognitive appraisal, changing action tendencies toward maladaptive emotions, preventing emotional avoidance (that is, response prevention), and using emotional exposure procedures. From the emotional science literature, UP imports the notion of addressing deficits in emotion regulation, as these seem to be ubiquitous in the mood disorders (except for bipolar disorder). We will look at this model in detail in the next section, noting the overlap with the McKay et al. (2011) approach regarding exposures.

CONTENT OF THE UNIFIED PROTOCOL

The UP (Barlow et al., 2011) is intended to take place over twelve to eighteen sessions, each lasting fifty to sixty minutes and occurring on a weekly basis (though later sessions may be spaced two weeks apart). Clients have a workbook (Barlow et al., 2010) to guide them through the process, with Barlow et al. (2011) being the therapist's step-by-step guide, suited to most mental health professionals. The treatment progresses through eight modules that begin with enhancing motivation and understanding emotions, continue through modules covering the five core skills described below, and conclude with a module for summary, maintenance, and relapse prevention.

The UP (Barlow et al., 2011) focuses on emotions, helping clients learn to confront and experience uncomfortable emotions and respond to them more adaptively (without avoidance or other ineffective strategies). Clients are taught early in the protocol that emotions have three components (physiological, cognitive, and behavioral) that interact in emotional experience. This sets the stage for the first core skill in the model: emotion awareness. A second skill teaches clients to challenge their appraisals of external and internal threats and thus to grow in cognitive flexibility. The third set of skills is to identify and modify maladaptive action tendencies, or "emotion-driven behaviors" (Barlow et al., 2011, p. 19). It is here that exposure therapy appears to work, as it helps prevent these action tendencies.

McKay et al. (2011) suggest some types of emotion avoidance strategies that would be incorporated under action tendencies (though some may be closer to *in*action tendencies). For depression, a person might sleep, use alcohol or drugs, distract herself, avoid social contact, or ruminate. A person with anger might be aggressive, shut down, use alcohol or drugs, or ruminate about events that triggered the anger. Persons with excessive shame might also avoid people or activities associated with feelings of shame. They might withdraw, suppress their shame with anger, or ruminate about shameful situations. McKay et al. (2011) suggest these are the actions to be avoided (responses to be prevented) when engaging in imaginal exposures.

Tolerance of physical sensations is the fourth skill of the UP. Barlow et al. (2011) stress that exposure to physiological symptoms (interoceptive exposure) should be relevant to the person's symptoms, that the sensations evoked by the exposure should be strong, and that exercises should be done repeatedly, both in and out of session. McKay et al. (2011) supplement this with some good suggestions that are incorporated into the menu in Part II of this book.

The final skill set of UP is bringing the first four together through emotion exposure exercises that elicit the emotion through internal and situation cues. The authors stress that the situation must be confronted fully without resorting to avoidance behaviors or other action tendencies. Some exercises may be done in the office, consistent with the imaginal exposures in the McKay et al. (2011) manual, though the emphasis is more on the emotional experience than the cue that elicits it. Barlow et al. (2011) suggest the exposures follow a stepwise hierarchy, but one may also move to more challenging situations sooner if the client is able. Once again, it is key that these produce new learning that the emotions are not as dangerous or debilitating as the client previously thought. Both the workbook for UP (Barlow et al., 2010) and the McKay et al. (2011) manual offer other specific protocols for exposure.

Looking Ahead

The flexibility of exposure and response prevention as techniques is truly extraordinary. As they evolve from the early animal models through CBT and a third generation of therapies, they are fortified by contexts that extrapolate effectiveness beyond the purely behavioral. Expanding the use of these techniques beyond the anxiety spectrum further contributes to their viability as important tools in any therapist's box.

Part II

A Menu of Specific Suggestions for Exposure and Response Prevention

CHAPTER 9

Using the Exposure Menu in Context

We have come quite a way in our journey of understanding exposure therapy (ET) and response prevention (RP) and their iterations in a variety of broader therapeutic approaches. We have seen that there is a variety of ways to adapt ET into differing therapy packages, for ET is at its root a technique, not a model of therapy. Still, ET and RP exist to help individuals who are struggling with anxiety, and their use and effectiveness in that arena is what matters most to clinicians. As I observed early on, one of the several hindrances to using ET is the gap between its basic theory and fitting it to individual needs. No two persons who experience excessive anxiety are alike, nor are their symptoms or their resources for tolerating and profiting from ET.

A major goal of this book is to provide therapists with a detailed list of options for exposures to many of the most common manifestations of anxiety; this follows in Part II. This is intended to save therapists time and creative energy as it offers a number of suggestions for exposure to many fears. It is by no means comprehensive, nor is it meant to be simply cut and pasted into an exposure hierarchy. However, I hope it will give you ideas and spur creative application of ET and RP techniques to the needs of individual clients.

The goals of this brief chapter are twofold. First, we will consider how to contextualize ET and RP into the major therapies mentioned thus far. Then, I will flesh out the basic exposure plans of Chapter 4 to give guidance on how to most effectively utilize the suggestions that follow.

Contextualizing Exposure Therapy

Since ET, though supported as an evidence-based treatment, is actually a technique and not an overall treatment theory or model, it can be used rather flexibly. It's fair to say that not many patients who enter clinicians' offices fit the strict criteria of a single diagnosis and nothing else, and thus qualify for manualized treatment. In addition, it is far easier for a physician to determine if a person has strep or not than for a mental health professional to say a person has generalized anxiety disorder and nothing else. Therefore, it may be that the most effective use of evidence-based treatments is as modules (see for example Chorpita, 2007) that can be used or not on a case-by-case basis. I presented the basic strategy of doing ET and RP in Chapters 3 and 4 and then we saw how they can also be modules (in a somewhat informal sense) in broader CBT and DBT and ACT. We now look at a few more specifics on how to do this in your practice.

Formulating Treatment: How Much Is Enough?

One tension in developing a treatment plan for a client is to provide the most help at the least expense, both in terms of money spent and in terms of the valuable time and energy clients spend in coming to therapy. For instance, many clients greatly enjoy just having someone to listen to them and may deflect the work of therapy by using it as a context for support alone. This may fit into some models, such as nondirective therapies, but ethical concerns arise about having third parties pay for their insureds to just have someone to talk to. Moreover, some models of therapy almost assume that major personality change is the key to therapeutic success. There is a place for extended long-term therapy, but generally it is not necessary for anxiety disorders unless they occur comorbidly with more severe problems or are overlaid with personality pathology.

However, an error that is not uncommon for those who use ET is rushing into the exposures so quickly that clients are overwhelmed and feel unsupported and so drop out of treatment. A vital truth about ET is that while it *is* effective, it is uncomfortable and thus easier in theory than in practice. Therapists who rush into ET without giving adequate support or enhancing the client's motivation may end up discouraging the client, leading to dropouts and even some clients' feeling more hopeless, since they could interpret their dropping out as having "failed" therapy.

Sources such as Clark and Beck (2010) give more details on assessment than I can focus on here. I offer a few recommendations for choosing an effective assessment strategy. First, there is no substitute for a thorough initial assessment. When anxiety disorders are rather simple and straightforward, promptly offering treatment can be attractive, because results can be substantial and quick. It is, however, often easier to find what you are looking for than to discover what is truly there. It is wise to enter any initial consultation with eyes wide open to comorbidities and situational aspects of the person's anxiety that might exacerbate the symptoms.

A good assessment should consider all possible diagnoses. Often anxiety disorders are comorbid with each other and with other disorders. As we saw in our discussion of DBT in particular, exposures may occur as a piece of treating a broader picture of diagnosed disorders as serious as borderline personality disorder. In contrast, an anxiety disorder could just be a simple phobia. A thorough interview should explore all other areas for possible disturbance. One important consideration if exposure therapy is indicated is to assess the individual's personal resources, both psychological and social.

The specifics of an assessment will depend on the broader therapeutic model into which exposure is placed. If you are doing CBT, for example, the procedures outlined in Clark and Beck (2010) will be helpful. Consistent with the cognitive focus of their model, objective assessments of anxiety (such as the Beck Anxiety Inventory [Beck & Steer, 1990]) will be part of the assessment, as will an assessment of the cognitions associated with anxiety, their triggers, and the beliefs that underlie them.

It is important to identify which symptoms are targets for these interventions and where they fall in an overall treatment plan. It will often be true that ET is not the place to start. One may need to address more acute issues and situations (such as suicidality or family crisis) before moving to ET and RP. This is particularly important in that ET and RP are difficult for clients, and building more trust with the counselor and growing stronger through progress in other areas may pave the way for greater success in ET.

Second, it is important to be thorough in addressing all fears and anxieties and to develop as detailed a list of avoidance/escape behaviors as possible, including both feared thoughts or feelings and external situations or events, actively enlisting the client in this process. While we hope for generalization to other feared items when doing exposures (and this does often occur), having a detailed list affords the best opportunity to start at a helpful place. Rating them on a detailed subjective units of distress scale (SUDS) of 1 to 100 can allow ranking of feared things to help plan where to step in first. It is often wise to allow the client to choose the first target for exposure, though the counselor will want to make sure that it is neither too hard nor too easy.

Finally, the client will benefit from a careful evaluation of personal strengths and motivations. Even if the diagnosis is clear and simple, it is critical to assess the qualities that will make ET and RP effective. To borrow a medical analogy, if a patient is in better general health, she may tolerate treatment better than if she is weak, albeit not diseased. In our case, desire to change must be high enough for the client to be willing to do exposures and give up safety behaviors. The therapist must educate the person that ET will be challenging, though ultimately most helpful, and encourage him to be realistic about the challenge so that he is adequately prepared. Doing imaginal exposure in the office can give some idea of the process. Other things to consider include social, spiritual, or motivational supports. Friends and family may be encouraging or quite the opposite. Faith and spirituality are for many people sources of strength that may be tapped during ET. There is a variety of resources that may enhance motivation, particularly concepts from DBT (such as mindfulness or distress tolerance) or ACT (such as willingness and values) that clients can draw on; summoning these will empower the individual to do the work of therapy.

So, "adequate therapy" in advance of exposure is whatever it takes to do a good assessment, establish thorough goals that touch on the breadth of anxieties, and place the therapy in context of any other disorders or life events that merit therapeutic intervention. There is no need to unload the therapeutic toolbox on all these, but neither should ET and RP be used without taking time to muster the psychological strength for it to succeed. Sometimes encouragement and a good treatment alliance are all that is necessary, but more often the client will benefit from time taken to develop a rationale for ET that makes sense (see Chapter 4) and to convene the individual's psychological supports. That is so if one is dealing with a fairly discrete anxiety issue; of course, broader therapeutic concerns may be in play, and we will look at those more below as we review some of the contextualization of ET and RP.

ET/RP on Its Own

A combination of ET/RP is its own empirically supported treatment for anxiety, though RP is incorporated only when avoidance/escape behaviors are strong, and particularly in OCD. We have seen how to structure ET as you build hierarchies from less to more anxiety evoking and have the patient expose herself to each anxiety-evoking situation until anxiety is significant and have her remain there until it abates. The purely behavioral form is most likely to be used with simple phobias in persons with no other significant pathology who are motivated to overcome the fear enough to do the exposure. Very highly motivated clients with more complicated anxieties may be able to tolerate ET in its purely behavioral form, though only if the therapist clearly explains how it works and the individual understands well enough so as not to escape mentally or physically during the exposures. Interoceptive exposure for panic and its symptoms can also be fairly behavioral once the symptoms are explained cognitively.

One purely behavioral aspect of RP that bears consideration for many anxieties is the differential reinforcement of other behaviors (DRO), and this can be useful with a variety of anxieties. Essentially, this is just rewarding oneself for not engaging in escape and avoidance behaviors. A person afraid of insects who will not take the garbage out to the can for fear of encountering bugs might reward himself with a favorite TV show or food if he doesn't ask his wife or child to take the trash out and instead does it himself. This is not likely to help him overcome his fear, but at minimum it makes it more concrete that the fear is "costing" him something. More details on using RP are discussed in Chapter 3.

ET/RP in the CBT Context

Most fears have cognitive components. While there are classically conditioned phobias and other fears that are physiological at the core, it is generally impossible to separate cognition from anxiety in humans. Even if life experience gives rise to anxiety, thoughts perpetuate it. In GAD in particular, nearly all of the fear is generated by cognition itself. So, ET/RP are well-placed in CBT as their home base, so to speak. Cognitive change lays a good foundation for behavioral change and thus can enhance ET and RP by increasing understanding of the need for them and by teaching coping strategies to occupy the mind properly while exposure is ongoing. Changing automatic thoughts and developing more effective self-statements hearten individuals for the task of exposure and stimulate resistance to the compulsion to escape anxious feelings. Clark and Beck (2010) provide a very thorough cognitive model of anxiety into which to place ET/RP.

Thus, CBT is almost a default therapeutic package into which ET and RP are integrated. As such, it is a suitable method for most anxiety disorders, especially those with a stronger cognitive component, such as GAD. It is more productive to consider when CBT may *not* be appropriate. Only some minor aspects of CBT (such as psychoeducation and realization of the irrationality of the fear) may need to precede ET/RP in simple phobias, so an entire course may be excessive in some rather clearly circumscribed situations.

At the other end of the continuum, some anxiety cases are too involved for CBT, such as when the fear is so overwhelming the client cannot manage to look at it rationally. Or CBT may be insufficient when the anxiety is overlaid with personality issues or suicidality. In such situations, a more intense mode of treatment is called for, and often that is DBT.

ET/RP in the DBT Context

Dialectical behavior therapy (Linehan 1993a, 1993 b) is designed for more troubled clients such as those with chronic suicidal and parasuicidal tendencies and those with BPD. It is appropriately intensive and multimodal in light of the population for which it was developed. As such, it is typically more than the common person with an anxiety disorder will need. As mentioned in Chapter 6, anxious persons can have more severe pathology, and severe pathology often includes anxiety, but in either of those cases anxiety may not be the primary target for the initial therapeutic intervention. This may also hold true for those who suffer with PTSD, which, though categorized as an anxiety disorder, can lead to severe pathology if the trauma was severe, frequent, or complex. For such severe PTSD cases, DBT may be a helpful model to consider.

Most persons with anxiety will not need DBT, but many and even maybe most can benefit from skills associated with DBT. Skills in mindfulness, emotion regulation, and distress tolerance are in particular relevant to ET/RP. When individuals seem ill-prepared to do exposures or to surrender escape behaviors, even if CBT has been tried, then teaching relevant skill modules from DBT can equip them to manage ET/RP more successfully. Therefore, the clinician is wise to add DBT skills before proceeding to exposures to improve the likelihood of success when working with those who need more skills to cope with the challenges of exposure.

ET/RP in the ACT Context

Whereas DBT has an eye toward greater pathology, ACT (Hayes et al., 2011) may be seen as slanted past pathology to a vision of overall well-being. Its stress on values and living a life in accord with one's values moves it almost past a treatment for psychopathology to a philosophy of life. It drinks deeply from the wells of spirituality and existential meaning to cast a vision for clients of a better life beyond merely being freed from the symptoms of anxiety. All of this is commendable to most any patient (or person in general). But most third-party payers want the "disorder" alleviated in the quickest way possible, and a full course of ACT may not be needed for this. While Hayes et al. (2011) eschew commitment to such a medical model, for many therapists it is a fact of life and a requisite for making a living.

Acceptance and commitment therapy can be helpful as an overall model when people's overall quality of life is severely impacted by their symptoms of anxiety—though not to the extent of suicidality or personality disorder. Anxiety can be so consuming that all focus and meaning is engulfed in fear and avoiding fear. Acceptance and commitment therapy provides an excellent model for patients whose anxiety is too complex for CBT but not severe enough for DBT. Exposure then can be carried out in the appropriate context of the overall model of ACT.

Acceptance and commitment therapy offers several perspectives that can be imported into a behavioral or CBT approach to enhance ET/RP. The philosophical stress on acceptance of suffering offers a helpful reframe of anxiety and the cycle of being anxious and worrying so as to avoid more anxiety. Since by definition ET and RP involve some discomfort, ACT moves this from a burdensome trial foisted on the client to an illustration of life—of how suffering is inevitable and to be accepted. Additionally, ACT's focus on values and living a life oriented by one's values moves basic ET past being a technique to alleviate anxiety to being a step in the direction of a better and more meaningful life. Response prevention, then, becomes a willing choice by the client to accept the fears and not attempt the impossible task of avoiding suffering. These aspects of ACT may easily be incorporated into the psychoeducational aspects of CBT without asking the client to undergo a full course of ACT.

These are only a few suggestions of how a counselor can move ET and RP into the context of broader therapeutic models or draw from these models to improve more basic approaches to exposure and response prevention. For all of the efforts toward manualization, psychotherapy will remain a creative and individualized process, and adapting empirically supported modules to mutually enhance one another for the patient's good is a balanced approach to scientific yet humane therapy.

Using the Menus in Part II

Part II offers what may be the most complete list of possible exposures available in one place, along with some potential targets for response prevention. These are meant to be a sort of buffet from which to choose exposures that fit individual clients, and not as set lists that everyone with a certain fear will need to complete. The counselor and client should explore the options together to see which is relevant and appropriate for the client's needs. This part of the book should be used as a resource, not a step-by-step guide for exposures and response prevention. Here I will offer a few suggestions on how best to utilize it.

Building Hierarchies Collaboratively and Experientially

Many common fears will be listed in Part II, with suggestions for different types of exposures and responses that might be targets for RP. Determination of which categories to work from is best made in collaboration with the client. One suggestion is to explore the client's anxieties first without consulting the lists that follow, first completing a thorough list of all feared items. These can then be arranged in a hierarchy from lowest to highest, according to their rating on a SUDS scale of 1 to 100. Typically exposures will proceed from the lowest to the highest, so long as the lowest is of enough concern to merit ET. A person might have a mild fear of balloons popping at a birthday party but no history of avoiding parties because of it. In such a case, ET is not really needed. Or, some fears may be rare and not an issue in everyday life so that even if the SUDS score is fairly high, they may not be important targets for ET. For example, a fear of snakes for a city dweller might rate a 60 on the SUDS scale, but be so rarely activated as to not merit ET until less severe fears that interfere more with daily life have been addressed. So do not be too rigid in just going from lowest to highest. Choosing targets, even after the SUDS rating sequences them, should be done collaboratively based on a balance of overall level of fear, relevance to the client's life, and readiness of the client to be exposed to them. Form 9.1 affords a format for triaging all fears.

Choosing the individual targets within a category is next. For example, a person has several fears, but fear of heights is the utmost priority given that the person avoids bridges and takes a circuitous route to work, costing time and money. The next step then is to devise the steps of the exposure hierarchy for this particular fear. Form 4.1, at the end of Chapter 4, is useful for this (its use is explained in Chapter 4). However, once the therapist and client have exhausted their ideas, consulting the list under Fear of Heights in Chapter 10 might afford some new ideas for exposures. If the client concurs any of these are relevant, then SUDS scores can be figured and the items added to the hierarchy appropriately. A key here is that clients may not think of imaginal, proprioceptive, or virtual reality exposures as readily as in vivo examples.

A similar procedure can be implemented for safety behaviors, supplementing those listed on Form 3.1 with any that are appropriate from the list provided in Part II.

Thinking Outside the Menu

The lists in the following chapters are partly designed to suggest helpful exposures, but they serve another purpose as well. Given that it is impossible to list every fearful situation, or to make one list fit all persons who fear a given situation, there is much room still for therapist creativity. Surveying the list of relevant fears with your client may stimulate additional ideas for exposure. It is often helpful to go through the list with the client to maximize the possibilities before settling on a hierarchy.

Another way the list may be used by the therapist is to stimulate creative thinking on exposures and RP in general. For those who work often with anxieties, systematically working through the lists may strengthen and broaden the network of associations in the therapist's mind and enhance innovative ideas for customizing exposures for clients. Like any other area of thought, the more examples and relationships one has in mind, the richer the associations that can produce novel expressions of that information.

In setting up exposures, work to make them vivid and personally relevant to the client. The more emotion they evoke, the more effectively they will serve the ends of exposure.

Moving from the Inside Out

As a rule, exposures move from the inside of the client out. That is, from imaginal exposures (in the mind), to emotional and proprioceptive ones (in the body), to seemingly real ones with virtual reality exposure, to actual exposures done "live." Not every one of these levels will be necessary for each client or each fear. Most often the stronger the fear, the more steps will be needed to lead to in vivo exposure. Also, as noted in Chapter 4, sometimes it is appropriate to move directly to in vivo exposure (assuming adequate work has been done to prepare the client adequately for the experience). Some clients, such as those with panic, will need to linger on interoceptive exposures while others will bypass those altogether. The vital point is to consider all aspects and then choose the steps that seem the fewest necessary to successfully navigate the client through ET.

The principle of inside-to-outside also applies to the physical locale of exposures. Early exposures often will be staged in the therapist's office and done with the therapist's supervision and support. These stages can be vital to building confidence for the client to move into the world. The therapist will ideally accompany the client on some in vivo exposures, for example meeting the client at the mall for an agoraphobic exposure, but this may not be practical in all cases. Family and friends can provide some of the early support until the client is able to face the fear on her own in the actual setting.

Managing Multiple Hierarchies

Earlier in this chapter we considered the need to be thorough in thinking through all areas of exposure for all of the client's fears before beginning, and we touched on triaging these to choose which to begin with, noting that it will not always be the easiest. This leaves a final question: whether the hierarchy of one fear should be completed before moving to another.

Here it is important to remember that being able to tolerate exposure is a skill that is learned. So, the approach should be comparable to how one learns any skill. Begin with a single fear, significant enough to be challenging, but not overwhelming. Proceed up that hierarchy until the client is not only tolerating rather high levels on the SUDS scale, but also states or shows signs of growing confidence in her ability to manage exposure exercises or to do without avoidance behaviors. The counselor may then consider continuing work on the initial fear hierarchy outside of sessions through homework or in vivo sessions, while introducing new fear hierarchies at lower levels in session. Soon, generalization may come into play and reduce the need to cover every step of every hierarchy. You can expect accelerating progress as therapy moves along, after things begin relatively slowly. It is important, though, not to give that expectation to clients, as they may feel they are failing in some ways if things do not progress as you suggested.

Client and therapist can collaboratively determine when it is time to decrease their sessions together as the client learns to manage his anxiety by using exposure and other skills that have been learned during the course of therapy. Weekly sessions can be reduced to every other week, with exposure homework still being completed between sessions. After several of these, move to once per month sessions for a couple of months. This is to continue accountability and reduce the likelihood of relapse. Some even might like a six-month follow-up session after regular treatment has ended. Much of this depends on progress not just in anxiety, but in the broader symptom picture and the management and support it may require.

Form 9.1 Hierarchy of Different Fears

This form allows you to summarize the entire list of your fears in one place, rating them based on the highest distress level you assign them. Remember, 1 is no anxiety or discomfort in thinking or doing it and 100 is absolutely intolerable distress. Your counselor may help you learn to judge when stresses are near 100 and when lower scores may be given, since often for the person feeling anxiety, many fears seem overwhelming. A second rating lets you score on a 1 to 10 scale how much a given fear is interfering with your daily life.

You will develop separate exposure hierarchies for each of these fears, but this form will help in planning where to begin working on the fears you experience. You will not necessarily begin with the least feared item or with the one that most interferes in daily life. Your therapist will guide you into wise choices on where to begin, and together you can complete the order of intervention column.

Fear	Type (feared place, object, situation, feeling, thought, or worry)	SUDS Score 1–100)	Interference Score (1–10)	Order of Intervention (complete with therapist)

CHAPTER 10

Exposure Therapy for Simple Phobias

As we have already seen, exposure therapies have their roots in the treatment of simple phobias and have long been found effective with these. So it is here we begin our menu of exposure ideas. On the DSM-5 development website (American Psychiatric Association, 2012), the core criteria for a specific phobia include a marked fear or anxiety about a specific object or situation (for example, flying, heights, animals, receiving an injection, seeing blood), with the phobic object or situation consistently provoking fear or anxiety and being actively avoided or endured with intense fear or anxiety. All of this is with the requisites that the fear is out of proportion (in accordance with its sociocultural context) to the actual danger posed by the feared object or situation and that the fear has lasted at least six months. The proposed content of DSM-5 specifies five major types of phobias: animal, natural environment, blood-injection-injury, situation, and other.

Phobias may be the anxiety disorders most suitable to pure behavioral exposure, though sometimes CBT or ACT principles may be engaged to empower the person to move through the exposures. We will also notice that many phobias lend themselves easily to in vivo exposures, though often starting with imaginal ones is wise.

Exposure Ideas for Simple Phobias

Animal Type

DOGS

Imaginal

- Imagine steps from in vivo section below

- Listen to recordings of barking dogs
- Watch video of calm dogs (such as a dog show)
- Watch video of dogs playing or wrestling

In Vivo

- Encounter small dog, leashed, in office (or behind fence in natural setting)*
- Approach small dog as closely as possible*
- Allow dog to lick hands*
- Be alone with small dog*
- Feed dog*
- Walk small dog outside (first with therapist then without)*
- Repeat above steps with large dog*
- Visit humane society*
- Go on walks where unleashed dogs might be encountered*
- Watch others (especially children) play with dog

(Items with * adapted from Thyer, 1981)

Response Prevention

- Changing sides of street when walking to avoid dogs
- Declining invitations to eat dinner with families with dogs
- Moving away from people walking dogs

CRAWLING INSECTS/SPIDERS

Imaginal

- Mentally picture spider/insect
- Describe spider/insect from memory
- Sing "Itsy Bitsy Spider" with hand motions

- Look at, then touch, pictures of spiders/insects
- Watch video of spiders/insects
- Handle rubber or plastic toy spider/insect
- Rub hairy fabric (Krijn, Emmelkamp, Olafsson, & Beimond, 2004)

In Vivo

(Use indigenous spiders/insects for all exposures)

- View spider/insect in jar*
- Approach spider/insect in natural setting*
- Catch spider/insect in a jar or similar
- Describe spider/insect to a friend as you observe it "live"
- Touch nonvenomous spider/insect; allow it to crawl on hand
- Clean cobwebs out of garage or basement

(Items with * adapted from Andersson et al., 2009)

FLYING INSECTS/BEES

Imaginal

- Picture target insect mentally
- Describe this mental image in detail
- Make buzzing sound of bee/insect (therapist may do this for client)
- Play recording of buzzing sound of bee/insect
- Watch video of insect/bee
- Look at/touch pictures of insect/bee*
- Look at/touch plastic insect/bee

In Vivo

- Look at dead insects/bees in plastic bag/jar*
- Carefully describe these insects/bees

- Touch dead insects/bees*
- Touch/hold live insects that do not bite/sting
- Allow insect to fly around office*
- Approach/observe honeybee on flower
- Knock down abandoned wasps' nest
- Turn over rock where insects may be hiding
- Visit beekeeper and watch hive

(Items with * adapted from Abramowitz et al., 2011)

Response Prevention

- Avoiding outdoor settings, bushes, basements, garages, picnics, and other places where insects might be flying

Natural Environment Type

HEIGHTS

Imaginal

- Imagine looking down from cliff, building's top floor, mall's upper level, and so on, *with* railing
- Imagine same *without* railing
- Imagine same while trying to describe detail at bottom of the precipice envisioned
- Picture riding up long escalator in an open area, or riding up in glass elevator
- Imagine standing on high diving platform at pool
- Look at pictures taken from airplanes, helmet cams of skydivers, or other high places
- Watch video taken from top of building or cliff
- Watch movies depicting action scenes on heights
- Watch IMAX or other high-resolution or 3-D movie where heights are depicted

Virtual Reality

- VR for fear of heights is an area with much research. Details on programs can be found in Krijn et al., 2004.

Proprioceptive

- Often heights create a feeling of dizziness, so see exposures under Fear of Dizziness in Chapter 12.

In Vivo

Several of the following can be done with or without holding on to a railing:

- Stand on balcony*
- Look over edge of a high place (cliff, top of tall building). Might begin inside building looking through glass then move to roof*
- Walk or run toward a railing with hands behind back*
- Run backward toward same*
- Ride up escalator
- Watch people bungee jump
- Ride roller coaster, Ferris wheel, or other high ride at amusement park
- Ride in glass elevator
- Stand on diving platform (and dive if historically able to do so)
- Walk across footbridge or swinging bridge

(Items with * adapted from Abramowitz et al., 2011)

Response Prevention

- Avoiding elevators, escalators, upper floors of malls, bridges, or tall buildings
- Changing travel routes to avoid hills or overlooks

STORMS

Imaginal

- Begin with single aspects of storms being imagined. Draw specifics from next item

- Imagine storm vividly, including dark clouds, sound of wind and rain, bolts of lightning and rumbles of thunder, and feel of wind and rain if one were out in the storm, and even picture a funnel cloud (therapist may guide imagery)
- Make audio recording of therapist guiding patient through this
- Do this to audio recording of an actual storm
- Write storm narrative, either recalling past storm or imagining worst-case scenario
- For hurricanes, pause in any of these variations for "eye" to pass and then go through steps again
- Add realism by adding sounds from recording, doing these near a fan to simulate wind, and/or having someone flash bright lights to simulate thunder. Recording of a train (without whistle) also simulates sound of a tornado
- Read magazine articles about storms, especially those including pictures and personal accounts
- Watch videos of various types of storms, or documentaries of same

In Vivo

- Visit location damaged by storm
- Go outside when bad weather is threatening or on blustery day
- Look out window and watch during storm
- Drive around in storm*
- Stand outside during storm

(Items with * adapted from Abramowitz et al., 2011)

Response Prevention

- Monitoring skies for clouds
- Monitoring weather reports excessively
- Changing plans due to threat of bad weather (unless advised to do so by weather report)

WATER

Imaginal

- Imagine looking at water from a distance, then drawing closer
- Wading at edge of pond or beach
- Stepping into pool
- Going under water (even holding breath to add more reality)
- Swimming
- Swimming too far into ocean and needing to be rescued by lifeguard
- Watch video of swimming in naturalistic setting (not a swim meet)
- Watch movies of water rescue or danger (such as *Baywatch* or *Jaws*, or scene from *The Abyss* where character is submerged in breathable fluid)
- Sit near pool or beach and watch others swim/dive

Interoceptive

- Hold breath for a while to simulate being underwater for a time

In Vivo

- Walk on bridge or pier over water
- Approach shore (if body of water) or shallow end (if pool)*
- Wade in water, or step into pool (holding ladder if available)*
- In pool, go underwater and resurface immediately*
- In ocean or lake, sit in shallow water
- Swim short distance to another person (in shallow water)*
- Swim underwater in shallow end for five seconds*
- In ocean or lake, swim into deeper water holding boogie board or other flotation aid
- Swim briefly in deep end or into water over one's head* (in pool one can do this near wall then move to middle of deep end)
- Jump from side of pool into shallow end*

- Jump from side of pool into deep end*
- Stand on end of diving board (with no intention of diving) until anxiety relents, then retreat
- Jump into pool from diving board*
- Dive into pool from diving board*

(Items with * adapted from Sherman, 1972)

Response Prevention

- Changing travel routes (walking or driving) to avoid passing over or near water

Blood-Injection-Injury Type

NEEDLES AND INJECTIONS

Imaginal

- Visualize being in physician's office and observing hypodermic needles in tray
- Reach over and pick one up
- Visualize pricking self with needle
- A nurse now gives you an injection in the shoulder; watch and describe what happens
- Imagine scene where blood is drawn from your arm. Therapist might describe in vivid detail (being as multisensory in description as possible). Audio recording might be given to client for work between sessions
- Pinch own finger
- Watch video explaining how to give injection or draw blood
- Watch video of person getting injection or blood drawn
- Watch video of surgery being performed

In Vivo

- Look at lancet or hypodermic needle
- Observe someone handling lancet or hypodermic needle

- Touch and handle lancet or hypodermic needle*
- Prick own skin with hypodermic needle
- Allow therapist or friend to prick skin with hypodermic needle
- Have qualified person perform a subcutaneous injection in the arm or vein puncture with saline solution*
- Receive acupuncture**
- Donate blood**

(Items with * adapted from Lilliecruetz, Josefsson, & Sydsjö, 2010; with ** from Abramowitz et al., 2011.)

Response Prevention

- Avoiding going to doctor with loved one
- Avoiding needed medical care

BLOOD

Imaginal

- Visualize blood on bandage
- Visualize cutting own finger
- Imagine helping friend with bloody nose
- Draw picture depicting blood with red crayon or marker
- View pictures of blood or wounds*
- Watch movie clips with scenes depicting blood*
- Watch videos of surgery showing blood*

(Items with * adapted from Abramowitz et al., 2011)

In Vivo

- Watch another person receive blood draw*
- Hold jar containing animal blood*

- Handle bloody piece of raw meat*
- Put fake blood on body and pretend it's real*
- Prick own finger with lancet*
- Observe a phlebotomist for extended time, handling vials

(Items with * adapted from Abramowitz et al., 2011)

Response Prevention

- Avoiding shopping for or cooking bloody meats
- Avoiding caring for self or loved ones properly if bleeding
- Not watching news or media if one thinks blood might be shown

MEDICAL PROCEDURES

Imaginal

- Picture having blood pressure taken at physician's office
- Picture outpatient office procedure such as having blood drawn or a minor surgical procedure
- Visualize simple medical procedure such as appendectomy. (Therapist can narrate procedure if client has difficulty doing so.) Include sounds of heart monitor beeps, metallic instruments clanking, voices of physician and others, plus possibly smell of anesthesia if surgery
- View pictures of such procedures*
- View videos of such procedures*

(Items with * adapted from Abramowitz et al., 2011)

In Vivo

- Sit in doctor's office*
- Walk through hospital*
- Sit on examination table*
- Observe another person undergoing medical procedures*

- Take own blood pressure, pulse, or temperature
- Visit physician for minor problem that doesn't require invasive procedure*
- Get a full physical (including as appropriate vaginal exam, prostate exam, and so on)*
- Undergo needed medical procedures*

(Items with * adapted from Abramowitz et al., 2011)

Response Prevention

- Refusing to get needed physical evaluations and procedures
- Avoiding going with family members for same
- Not visiting loved ones in hospitals or nursing homes

KNIVES

Imaginal

- Visualize looking at small knife
- Touch knife
- Hold knife
- Cut with knife
- Do above but with large knife/butcher knife
- Observe friend holding and using large knife
- Watch video of someone using knives to cook
- Watch video of knife thrower
- Write story of how you accidentally cut someone's finger with knife while cooking together

In Vivo

- Carry pocketknife
- Open and close pocketknife
- Look at and handle butcher knives*
- Place knives at home in spots where they are visible at all times*

- Visit cutlery shop*
- Visit Japanese steakhouse or other restaurant where knives are used in front of you
- Use knives to cut small items (peel a potato, for example)
- Use larger knives to cut meat
- Cook with friend if you fear accidentally cutting someone else, keeping knives between you two*

(Items with * adapted from Thyer, 1985)

Situational Type

FLYING

Imaginal

- Visualize steps of flying:
  - Packing
  - Leaving home or hotel room to go to airport
  - Riding to airport
  - Checking in
  - Going through security
  - Walking down jetway to plane
  - Sitting on plane
  - Taxiing
  - Taking off
  - Flying
  - Landing
  - Stress all senses: crowd noise in airport, hum of engines, smell of jet fuel as one boards plane, air blowing from nozzle above seat, and so on
- Vary scenario to include worst-case scenarios

- Read about airplanes
- Watch videos of planes taking off and landing
- Watch videos filmed inside planes
- Watch movies depicting problems on airplanes

Interoceptive

- If fear of motion sickness is part of the phobia, see Chapter 14 for ideas.

Virtual Reality

- Virtual reality (VR) is well-known as effective for fear of flying (Krijn et al., 2004), with Rothbaum, Hodges, Smith, Lee, and Price (2000) being an exemplary study. The VR simulations follow the flight through good and bad weather with speakers reproducing auditory stimuli that would be experienced. The VR exposures in the study were followed by in vivo ones.

In Vivo

- Go to airport; walk through terminal
- Watch planes take off and land*
- Sit in plane*
- Take flight

(Items with * adapted from Abramowitz et al., 2011)

Response Prevention

- Avoiding airports
- Not flying when it would be preferable

DRIVING

Imaginal

- Picture self sitting behind wheel of car
- Turn on engine, but remain in park
- Begin driving on straight road in good weather during daylight

- Change imagery to vary conditions (weather, day or night, fog, over bridges, mountain roads, and so on)
- Imagine worst-case scenario (for example, having an accident)
- Watch videos of racecars shot from inside cabins of cars
- Watch chase scenes from movies
- Play video games where person uses steering wheel to direct car

Virtual Reality

- Driving is another phobia with good support for VR (Krijn et al., 2004), and an exemplary article with information on the hardware used is Wald and Taylor (2003).

In Vivo

Items that follow can be done with or without a friend in the passenger seat. For some that will decrease anxiety but for others (fearing hurting others) it will be higher on the hierarchy:

- Sit behind wheel and start car
- Put car into gear but keep foot on brake and go nowhere

For the following, can add levels to match need: day versus night, good weather versus rainy versus snowy versus foggy*:

- Drive up and down driveway
- Drive slowly on quiet side street or in parking lots**
- Drive in familiar neighborhoods**
- Drive on city streets**
- Drive on highway*,**
- Drive during rush hour**
- Drive on freeway
- Drive unfamiliar or rental car

(Item with * adapted from Wald & Taylor, 2003; with ** from Abramowitz et al., 2011)

Response Prevention

- Having someone take the person places she would normally drive

- Taking other forms of transportation to avoid driving
- Selling or not repairing one's car to avoid driving
- Talking on phone to garner support during driving

BRIDGES

Imaginal

- Begin with imagined small bridge, like in garden
- Move the following steps from small bridge to one over lake or river:
    - Look at bridge from distance
    - Approach bridge
    - Watch as someone walks onto bridge
    - Walk onto bridge oneself
    - Walk across bridge looking straight ahead
    - Walk halfway across then pause and look over side for a minute before continuing
    - Use multiple senses: feel wind blowing, smell water below, hear traffic passing, feel coldness of railing, and so on
    - Imagine worst-case scenario (such as falling off)
    - Ride across bridge with another person driving
    - Drive across bridge (with and without passenger)
- Watch video of cars crossing bridges
- Watch video of individuals walking across bridges
- Watch movie scenes where drama occurs on bridges (cars hang off side, and so on)

Interoceptive

- Since a sensation of dizziness or vertigo may accompany this phobia, see Fear of Dizziness in Chapter 12.

In Vivo

- Follow steps of imaginal exposure above, but in actual settings (minus the worst-case scenario).

Response Prevention

- Changing travel routes to avoid bridges

TUNNELS

Imaginal

- Imagine looking at entrance to a tunnel
- Walk up to tunnel and peek into it, describing it
- Ride in car or train into tunnel
- Drive into tunnel
- Walk into tunnel and stroll through, observing details of the surroundings. Multisensory is important: smell the dampness, feel the cool or humid air, close eyes to simulate darkness, feel the walls, and so on
- Visualize going into a subway station then riding the subway
- Imagine worst-case scenario
- Look at pictures of tunnels, especially the long, underwater Chunnel between London and Paris
- Watch videos of going through tunnels

In Vivo

These may be done with or without a person accompanying:

- Walk under short overpass
- Walk through enclosed walkway without windows (for example, in back halls of mall or stadium)
- Ride amusement park ride featuring tunnel
- Approach tunnel outside car (if possible)*
- Get into car*

- Drive to place near tunnel and stop*
- Drive to tunnel opening, then one-quarter way in, then halfway, then through tunnel (if circumstances allow)*
- Ride subway

(Items with * adapted from Götestam & Svebak, 2009)

Response Prevention
Changing travel routes to avoid tunnels or similar places

ENCLOSED PLACES (ELEVATORS)

Imaginal

- Picture self in closet with door open, then closed
- Picture self standing on small balcony
- Picture self in small room without windows, with walls that close in
- Visualize walking into cave through small entrance and down into caverns far from entrance, then with flashlight/lamp burning out
- Visualize getting into glass elevator and going up only one floor
- Visualize getting into glass elevator that goes up several floors
- Repeat last two in elevator without any windows
- Imagine elevator getting stuck
- Do these alone and with others on elevator (crowds may make this easier or harder, depending on individual)

Interoceptive

- Often this fear is associated with feelings of suffocation or hyperventilation; see Fear of Hyperventilation/Shortness of Breath in Chapter 12.

Virtual Reality

- VR has been used for fear of enclosed places (Krijn et al., 2004), with scenarios for balconies, small gardens, small rooms with or without windows or doors, inward-moving walls, and elevators.

In Vivo

- Remain in small bathroom closet, backseat of car, sleeping bag, and so on*
- Wear turtleneck or scarf*
- Wear handcuffs or cover body with heavy blanket*
- Drive in large rush-hour traffic jam
- Enter elevator; push button to keep door open; then exit
- Enter closet and have friends come in until person is crowded into back corner of closet
- Follow in reality the steps for elevators in the imaginal section above
- Put self in CT or MRI machine, or enclosed tanning bed

(Items with * adapted from Abramowitz et al., 2011)

Response Prevention

- Taking stairs rather than elevator
- Sleeping or staying in room with door open
- Avoiding medical procedures involving machines that make one feel trapped
- Avoiding more efficient travel route if one feels enclosed in traffic or on certain roads

Other Phobias

CHOKING

Imaginal

- If phobia originated with actual incident of choking, create narrative of that story
- Imagine chewing food that's hard to swallow
- Imagine gagging on bite of food
- Imagine actually choking; use many sensations: urge to cough, fullness in throat, taste of food in mouth, and so on
- Imagine this for private setting, then a public one (order depends on which is lower in hierarchy for the individual)

- Look at pictures of persons choking
- Watch lighthearted choking in video (for example, the scene in *What about Bob?*)
- View instructional video on Heimlich maneuver
- View video of graphic choking

In Vivo

Move setting from private to public settings as you proceed:

- Pretend to be gagging
- Pretend to be choking
- Depending on how much avoidance of eating certain foods is present, eat foods rather dissimilar to ones that are feared/avoided
- Eat dry bread without water
- Eat foods similar to avoided foods
- Eat avoided foods
- Eat avoided foods and fill mouth with them

Response Prevention

- Avoiding restaurants or other public places to eat
- Avoiding certain foods associated with the fear

NAUSEA

In many cases, nausea is feared because it is associated with the possibility of vomiting, so many exposures will be more for vomiting itself. See Fear of Vomiting, below, for many applicable exposures. It is also important to bear in mind that actual nausea may be caused by the arousal of anxiety toward some other stimulus. Still, often the person then becomes anxious about the nausea as well.

Imaginal

- Describe in detail feelings associated with nausea, including indigestion, acidity, gas, queasy stomach, feeling flushed, and so on. Make as vivid as possible
- Imagine you just ate something that would make you nauseous (drank sour milk, ate undercooked meat, and so on)

- For secondary nausea: describe experience of nausea when imaginally exposed to other feared stimuli

Interoceptive

- See those under Vomiting

In Vivo

- See those under Vomiting
- Wear belt too tight to create awareness of pressure in belly
- Drink a lot of soda to create gassy feeling from carbonation
- Watch gory movie if sight of blood and gore nauseates you

Response Prevention

- Avoiding eating certain foods
- Taking antacids or other medicines preventively
- Avoiding activities (such as exercise) that might lead to nausea

VOMITING

Imaginal

- Visualize seeing a stranger throw up (with follow-up including how others reacted and how the scene ended)
- Visualize seeing someone close to you throw up*
- Visualize throwing up*
- Create narrative and imagine scene of an incident where you actually threw up*
- Make script of scenario where you vomit; audiorecord for rehearsal*
- View pictures, then videos, of vomit or someone vomiting*
- Create fake vomit from vegetable soup or the like*
- Make vomiting noises: therapist, then client, then friends of client in natural environment*

- Pretend to vomit with sounds and motions, following same pattern as previous item*
- Expose self to stale or strong cheese odor for olfactory exposure*
- Taste vomit-flavored jelly beans; then mix these with other jelly beans to make them less predictable*

Interoceptive

- Spin around*
- Ride playground or amusement park ride that goes in circles
- Hold tongue depressor on back of tongue for thirty seconds (from Forsyth et al., 2008)

In Vivo

- Fill mouth very full until you feel gag reflex
- Eat, then do physical activity*
- Drink water until you feel full*
- Put finger to roof of mouth and slide toward back of throat*
- Have friends/family surprise client between sessions by pretending to vomit*

Response Prevention

- Avoiding eating things client believes will make her nauseous (and increase risk of vomiting)
- Avoiding going places that might stimulate nausea

(Items with * adapted from Smith, 2010)

LOUD NOISES

Imaginal

- Picture scenes where one might encounter loud noises (for example, sitting near train tracks, at picnic where fireworks start, or at child's party with balloons popping)
- Client augments this imagery by making loud noise
- Therapist interrupts this imagery with sudden noises simulating feared item

- Make audio recording of quiet music randomly interrupted by loud noise (choose noise relevant to client)
- Watch videos or movies with sudden loud noises (gunshots, explosions, shouting, sirens, and so on)
- Watch same, but with back turned to the screen so noises are less anticipated

In Vivo

- Go to places that were pictured in first imaginal exposure above
- Immerse self in loud noise such as by being in crowded mall or factory or near airport runway, train yard, or active day care
- Play game where client and friends sit on balloons to try to pop them
- Roll window of car down in heavy traffic
- Invite others to surprise client with sudden shouts of "boo!" or intermittent loud claps
- Have person sounding air horn at irregular intervals in another part of house
- Set phone to ring with irritating noise and at loud volume

Response Prevention

- Any situations avoided for fear of noise (malls or large stores, ball games, airports, and so on)
- Any preventive measures to soften sound, such as ear plugs at ball games

TRASH

Imaginal

- Picture trash can in an office with only paper in it
- Move to image of garbage can in kitchen with some food leftovers in it
- Move to image of outdoor Dumpster; imagine odor, and flies buzzing around it
- Peek inside Dumpster to see restaurant refuse such as chicken bones, grease, soured liquids, coffee grounds, and so on; keep this multisensory
- Finally, reach into Dumpster and pull out food trash with flies on it

- View pictures of trash
- View pictures or videos of slums around the world that are full of trash and quite unsanitary
- Pretend to have gag response to above

In Vivo

- Follow early items above, except actually approach the trash in these settings
- Spill some trash in yard or on patio and clean up by hand
- Take something to dispose of at nearby landfill
- Pick up litter in run-down part of town

Response Prevention

- Circumventing areas when walking or driving where there might be trash
- Having other persons handle trash the client is responsible for
- Not taking out garbage

URINE

Imaginal

- Visualize urine on floor next to toilet
- Visualize urine on toilet seat that you must wipe before using
- Imagine self to be a nurse who must carry urine sample bottles one at a time from one room to another
- In doing this, notice there is some urine on side of a specimen bottle, but only after you picked it up
- Imagine picking up dirty laundry and noticing yellow stain on partner's underwear
- Imagine having to clean toilets and floor near them with sponge and no gloves
- Visualize sitting on toilet only to sense wetness due to urine being on it
- View pictures of urine or video of person urinating

In Vivo

- Visit humane society, kennel, or zoo where smell of urine is strong
- Touch plunger or toilet seat
- Touch genitals after urination without washing hands (Abramowitz et al., 2011)
- Clean toilets at home
- Use public restroom
- Change baby's diaper
- Pick up dirty laundry
- Handle specimen jar with urine in it
- Urinate on piece of cloth and expose self to odor several times a day

Response Prevention

- Avoiding handling laundry
- Refusing to use certain restrooms
- Overly sanitizing toilets
- Not changing diapers if responsible for doing so

CHAPTER 11

Exposure Therapy for Social Anxiety Disorder

What is the most common anxiety disorder? According to Hofmann and Barlow (2002) it is social anxiety disorder (SAD) and, moreover, it is the third most common of all mental disorders. Their review found that it has a lifetime prevalence of 13.3 percent and often follows a chronic course while taking a toll by impairing vocational and social functioning. Treating such a common and debilitating disorder well is important.

Note that for the upcoming DSM-5 (American Psychiatric Association, 2012), it is proposed that the name be "social anxiety disorder," with "social phobia" in parentheses, reversing these terms from DSM-IV (American Psychiatric Association, 2000). Bögels et al. (2010) make this recommendation after determining that calling it a "phobia" is misleading in comparison to simple phobias. There are relatively few changes to the actual diagnostic criteria, though debate over whether there are subtypes and what these are continue. As of this writing, the DSM-5 site (American Psychiatric Association, 2012) lists three subtypes. *Generalized* refers to those who fear a wide range of social situations, though there is question as to how broad this needs to be for inclusion. *Performance* subtype refers to those who are only socially anxious when asked to do something in front of others, such as speaking. This is debated, as Bögels et al. (2010) conclude that this fear is qualitatively different from SAD, though they still see it as worthy of being a subtype or indicator. Finally, *selective mutism*, a disorder most often found in children and marked by a refusal to speak to others in public, can be seen as a possible subtype of SAD (Bögels et al., 2010) and is at this point included as the third.

Hoffman and Barlow (2002) trace the core symptoms of SAD back into history and maintain that public speaking is still the primary venue for the presence of the disorder. Central to the symptoms is whether the individual must do something knowing that others may be watching, or even to an extent evaluating, what he does. This causes a degree of anxiety (fear of being embarrassed, humiliated, and so on) out of proportion to what might be expected for that situation according to cultural norms. It is also important to note that symptoms include fear of showing physical signs of anxiety in the situation, such as blushing or trembling (Bögels et al., 2010). Social anxiety disorder appears to be more common among women in the community, but men present for treatment as often as women do. While some have speculated that persons with SAD are deficient in social skills, Hoffman and Barlow find that the literature supports this being more of a perception (a cognitive distortion, if you will) than a reality.

Persons with SAD benefit from CBT and ET (Hoffman & Barlow, 2002), with a combination of the two likely being the best when compared to controls (Barlow et al., 2002), though social skills training may be appropriate when there actually is a deficit in these. Cognitive distortions that may contribute are underestimating one's skills and ability, overestimating the social threat and cost, and miscalculating the likelihood of making the social blunder that is dreaded. There may also be tendencies toward bias in what is remembered or perceived so that the anxiety is exacerbated.

Exposures for SAD will often be in the context of CBT, though Hoffman and Barlow (2002) note that exposure alone can be helpful as well. Generally DBT will be unnecessary, but as we see in many of the anxieties, choosing to teach several of the skills of DBT can strengthen the tolerance for exposure. Acceptance and commitment therapy can add helpful contexts for exposures. For example, a client who aspires to be an attorney as a value must accept the anxieties of speaking in front of others and be willing to accept some negative outcomes.

Most exposures will be steps toward the feared situations, though some interoceptive exposures are useful here when the client fears the symptoms of blushing, sweating, or trembling that may accompany SAD.

There is a range of avoidance or escape behavior (or experiential avoidance) for SAD that merits careful evaluation as the therapist integrates response prevention into treatment.

Some suggestions for exposures follow.

Exposure Ideas for SAD

PUBLIC SPEAKING/PERFORMANCE

Imaginal

- Sitting in empty auditorium
- Sitting in auditorium and listening to speaker
- Standing at podium in empty auditorium
- Reciting planned speech or poem at podium of empty auditorium
- Doing previous while imagining friends and family are only ones in auditorium
- Reciting planned speech or poem before friendly, supportive crowd

- Reciting planned speech or poem before rather disinterested crowd
- Reciting planned speech or poem before hostile crowd
- Giving speech and microphone goes out, gets feedback, or is far too loud
- Giving speech and you freeze
- All of preceding can be imagined in smaller setting such as classroom or small group such as school or church committee meeting
- Singing/playing instrument through sequence of first eight suggestions
- Singing at karaoke bar
- Apply dancing or other performance area to first eight suggestions
- Present idea to imaginary committee at workplace
- Therapist creates story of client speaking in front of group in presence of client
- Conversely, more creative clients might tell or write their own story. Record story for practice exposure at home
- Videotape speech and review alone/with others, and/or post to YouTube
- Watch speech on Internet and imagine being the speaker

Virtual Reality or Technology Assisted

- Deliver speech before virtual audience on video, including supportive, neutral, and negative audiences (Anderson, Rothbaum, & Hodges, 2003; note they utilize special equipment to increase perception of reality of audience)
- Deliver speech in front of virtual auditorium that is empty, filling, or full, with supportive or negative audience (Harris, Kemmerling, & North, 2002)

In Vivo

- Exercise in crowded gym*
- Give speech*
- Make toast*
- Eat alone in crowded restaurant*

- Sign check or complete application with others watching*
- Speak up at meeting*
- Interview for job*
- Do first five imaginal items in real auditorium; actually *do* deliver speech/poem
- Answer or ask questions in class
- Go to city or town hall community meeting and ask questions or add comments to discussion
- Order something that you cannot pronounce at a restaurant
- Give speech or perform in front of mirror
- Record self singing at karaoke recording booth
- Sing at karaoke bar
- Go ice skating at busy rink
- Go out of your way to speak to boss
- Ask someone for a date
- Join Toastmasters International or similar organization where you might practice speech-giving

Response Prevention

- Avoiding public settings or meetings that evoke thoughts of personal performance
- Some might avoid malls, neighborhood meetings, small groups, clubs, discussion classes, bars, concerts, singing in church, going back to school, applying for jobs or going for interviews, etc.

(Items with * adapted from Abramowitz et al., 2011)

BEING LOOKED AT/BEING THE CENTER OF ATTENTION

Imaginal

- Many examples from Public Speaking/Performance can be adapted
- Having your name called to win door prize at party

- Being approached by television crew to give opinion on current event
- Being called out for praise at church, civic group, or business meeting
- Hearing friend bragging about you in group of friends
- Being chosen from audience to assist magician or other performer

In Vivo

- Ask question in class*
- Drop change in public*
- Speak loudly*
- Wear unusual or out-of-place clothing*
- Join aerobics class*
- Go to restaurant where your name is called when your table is available
- Make or second motion in meeting
- Volunteer to read minutes in meeting, read text in worship, or make announcements at gathering
- Deliberately make eye contact with strangers and say "hello"

Response Prevention

- Avoiding settings where one might be noticed or recognized: restaurants, malls, parties, meetings, and so on
- Intentionally wearing bland clothing or not grooming to one's best to avoid comment

(Items with * adapted from Abramowitz et al., 2011)

EMBARRASSMENT/FEELING FOOLISH

Imaginal

- Going to fast-food restaurant in formal attire (this and several others can later be done in vivo as well)
- Giving wrong answer to question orally in class

- Opening wrong door and intruding on meeting
- Being at crowded concert or sports event and usher tells you to move because you are in wrong seat
- Being on bus and realizing your fly is unzipped or your blouse is unbuttoned
- Someone in the mall tells you your clothes look funny or comments on your appearance in derogatory way
- Spilling bag of groceries as you walk out of store
- Accidentally belching loudly at funeral

In Vivo

- Ask directions to obvious location*
- Order item at restaurant that is clearly not on menu (or product of another restaurant)*
- Incorrectly answer question in class*
- Mispronounce word intentionally in conversation*
- Slip or fall in crowded area*
- Drop some coins on floor in public area*
- Attempt to purchase something without enough money*
- Try to be as boring as possible in conversation, or make strange statements*
- For men, stand at urinal in busy restroom and feign not being able to urinate*
- Call out floors in crowded elevator*
- Eat something messy (such as boiled lobster) in formal restaurant
- Wear opposing team's colors to big game
- Go in public with hair mussed and sloppy clothes
- Ask someone you are familiar with to remind you of her name
- Call people on telephone and talk rather than e-mailing or texting them

(Items with * are adapted from Abramowitz et al., 2011)

Response Prevention

- Avoiding activities that might lend themselves to mistakes: going to restroom in public, eating in public, making eye contact, phoning people rather than e-mailing them

CRITICISM

Imaginal

- Getting paper back from teacher that says negative things about your work
- Meeting with boss and getting a bad review (add specifics based on client fears)
- Romantic partner complaining about your clothes, appearance, fragrance, or favorite musician
- Parent criticizing way you care for him/her
- Dinner guest complaining his food isn't cooked properly
- Friend or family member complaining you bought her a bad gift
- Comedian picks on you at nightclub performance

In Vivo

It is not realistic to create many situations of being criticized. For example, you would not ask the client to do poorly on her job to elicit a complaint from her boss. So, only a few ways a "live" criticism might be staged are offered.

- Therapist pretends to be boss and criticizes job performance
- Ask friend or family member to surprise you with criticism during week (making sure that person chooses one she doesn't really mean)
- Pull out papers from school/college and review negative remarks of teachers
- Write out some self-criticisms and have therapist, friend, or family member read them back to you

Response Prevention

- This is another fear that may not be avoided directly by effort, but explore with your client ways that he goes out of his way to avoid criticism or negative comments, such as over-cleaning the house before having guests over or avoiding any interactions that might be evaluated negatively.

OFFENDING OTHERS

Imaginal

- Forgetting something someone told you when she asks you about it
- Accidentally saying something bad about person you are talking to or about a person loved by that person
- Making political comments you know will upset other person
- Inviting someone to dinner, serving pork, and realizing your guest is Jewish (or serving meat to vegetarian)
- Making disparaging remark about friend's car, clothing, or home
- Making sexist or racist remark
- Telling server at a restaurant that your meal was not as good as expected, or salesperson that his merchandise is of poor quality
- Giving someone a holiday present that is clearly less expensive than the one that person gave you

In Vivo

- Return item to store*
- Send food back at restaurant*
- Drive slowly in fast lane on highway (though taking care not to cause an accident)*
- Slowly use ATM machine when others are waiting to use it*
- Pay at a convenience store or fast-food restaurant with lots of change, counting it out slowly
- Tell someone who said something unkind to you she hurt your feelings
- Tell coworker you would prefer that he not do something that annoys you (or be assertive in other ways that are appropriate albeit risky)
- "Defriend" someone or decline "Friend" request on social networking site
- Decline to do someone a favor when asked (encourage partner or friend to ask a favor randomly to set this up)
- Complain to customer service about your phone, Internet, television, or other service, over phone or ideally in person

Response Prevention

- Doing things to prevent offending anyone: failing to speak up if someone cuts in line, taking on coworker's responsibilities at work rather than speak up to the coworker, and so on

(Items with * adapted from Abramowitz et al., 2011)

SOCIAL EVENTS/PARTIES

Imaginal

- Going to formal party and being dressed very casually
- Walking into party and everyone stops talking and stares
- Arriving for party and host says you came on wrong day
- Arriving at party and realizing no one you know is there
- Trying to join conversation at party and being ignored
- Going to costume party and forgetting to wear costume, or wearing costume and finding out it's *not* a costume party
- Forgetting names of people at party after they call you by name
- Struggling to think of what to say to keep conversation going
- Someone speaks to you who knows you, but you cannot remember ever meeting that person
- At formal dinner party, not knowing right fork to use, or how to gracefully eat entrée
- At dinner party, entrée is something you cannot eat
- At event, someone makes uncomfortable amorous advances to you
- In therapy, imagine entire process of asking someone on date and walk through date; perhaps use role-play to enhance exposure

In Vivo

- Host small party
- Go to small party with close friends/family

- Initiate conversations with people at work, in neighborhood, or in social group you do not know well to rehearse this skill for social events. Especially consider entering groups that are already discussing something
- Go to party/gathering with friend who is more socially confident; make forays to talk with others on your own during party
- Go to meetings of book clubs, special interest groups, and so on
- Watch sports event at sports bar
- Go to classes or small groups at your church, community center, library, and so on
- Go to weddings you might usually have skipped
- Visit funeral home, wake, or memorial service when friend's loved one dies
- Ask salespeople for help and ask questions
- Go to party on your own where you know few people
- Ask someone out on a date

Response Prevention

- Avoiding events that client is invited to or activities he might like; for example, wanting to learn tennis but being reluctant to attend classes to learn
- Avoiding social situations due to fear of sensations associated with embarrassment or anxiety. Interoceptive exposures may help the person become more accepting of these and less anxious about experiencing them—see Chapter 12 for more of these

TREMBLING

Imaginal

For persons who fear trembling, choose the situations in the suggestions in this chapter that are appropriate, adding that in that context the person starts to tremble.

- Imagine trembling in front of others in multiple settings

Interoceptive

- Tense muscles to create sensation of trembling
- Stand in cold until you tremble

SWEATING

Imaginal

For persons who fear sweating, choose appropriate situations from the suggestions earlier in this chapter, adding that in that context the person starts to sweat.

- Sweating in front of others, particularly those you might fear seeing you sweat (perspiring on a date or when talking to someone to whom you are attracted)
- Feeling dampness under your arms during job interview
- Being in a warm room and feeling beads of perspiration on your forehead as you talk with someone you do not know well
- Doing something active with another person that induces sweat (running, playing golf, tilling a garden, and so on)

Interoceptive

- Turn heat higher or air conditioning lower to induce sweat in counseling office, then at home when around others
- Exercise to induce perspiration
- On a day off from work, do not put on antiperspirant

BLUSHING

Imaginal

- For persons who fear blushing, choose appropriate situations in suggestions earlier in this chapter, adding that in that context the person starts to blush.

Interoceptive

- If compliments induce blushing, therapist tries that in session
- Letting cool wind blow on face or leaving face exposed while outside on cold day if these induce "blush"

CHAPTER 12

Exposure Therapy for Panic Disorder and Agoraphobia, with a Focus on Interoceptive Exposure

Panic disorder is characterized by the physical sensations of anxiety and the misinterpretation of these somatic symptoms (Koch, Gloster, & Waller, 2007). In such cases, the person fears fear itself, which can lead to a debilitating feedback loop where anxiety creates physical symptoms, which cause increased anxiety. These result in panic attacks and thus panic disorder when the person becomes excessively concerned with the recurrence of panic attacks. As of this writing, it is proposed for DSM-5 (American Psychiatric Association, 2012) that agoraphobia be no longer linked exclusively to panic disorder but can be coded by itself. In the past, it was assumed that fear of panic attacks in public led individuals to stay away from places to avert panic attacks or at least ensure that should they occur the person would be in a safe, private environment. The proposed change in DSM-5 acknowledges that some people can fear public places but not necessarily have panic disorder. Agoraphobia is present if at least two places are excessively feared due to anxiety about panic or other incapacitation so that if another person (as a safety cue) is not present the situations are only endured with extreme anxiety. The exercises in this chapter also may often be useful to prepare for difficult exposures when treating PTSD.

For panic, exposures will focus on the symptoms that come with panic and how they can be created deliberately. These exposures are sometimes useful with other fears, but I list them here as this is the most common usage for them. We then turn to the five major categories of places feared and avoided in agoraphobia, suggesting exposures for examples of each. The only tool needed is the client's body, so these are all in vivo exposures. While typically hierarchies are not used with these (Koch et al., 2007), it is common to begin with low-intensity experiences and move to stronger sensations. Many of these exposures can create more than one symptom of panic, so they are listed under symptoms they are most likely to produce.

Interoceptive Exposure Ideas for Panic Disorder

For all interoceptive exposures, items with * are adapted from Abramowitz et al., 2011, and with ** from Forsyth et al., 2008.

DIZZINESS

- Shake head side to side*
- Roll head from shoulder to shoulder at two or more rotations every thirty seconds*
- Spin while sitting or standing (with or without eyes closed); rate of one rotation every two seconds for thirty seconds*
- Hold breath*
- Spin on playground spinner or amusement park ride

HYPERVENTILATION/SHORTNESS OF BREATH

- Take deep and rapid breaths at one every two seconds for sixty seconds*
- Rebreathe expired air from bag**
- Put head between legs**
- Breathe through straw, using small cocktail size straw: pinch nose and breathe as long as possible, take quick breath and repeat; at least sixty seconds, minimum two trials*
- Climb steps**

HEART PALPITATIONS/INCREASED HEART RATE

- Run in place*
- Jog while lifting knees high*
- Do push-ups*

DEPERSONALIZATION/DEREALIZATION

- Stare at self in mirror*

- Stare at small dot on wall*
- Sit in dark room with strobe light*
- Stare at moving spiral*
- Stand in dark room or wear blindfold with soundproof headphones*
- Stare at fluorescent lights*

SWEATING

- Wear heavy clothes in hot room while exercising
- Stand near space heater
- Visit sauna

Response Prevention

- Taking medications to escape any of the feelings above
- Avoiding situations that might evoke these sensations
- Seeking reassurance from others that symptoms are not dangerous

Exposure Ideas for Agoraphobia

Krijn et al. (2004) document the effectiveness of virtual reality technology-assisted exposures for agoraphobia, encompassing settings such as supermarkets, beaches, a dark barn with a black cat, a covered bridge, and a town square.

BEING OUTSIDE ALONE

Imaginal

- Visualize walking outside your home briefly, such as to get mail or retrieve something from car
- Walking down street and around block back to house or apartment
- Getting out of car and walking in field or large park

- Walking on trail in woods
- And then getting lost on that trail
- Being in foreign airport and getting lost in terminal
- Floating alone in hot air balloon
- Watch videos about explorers who went places alone (such as sailor navigating around world in one-person boat)

In Vivo

- Try the first four imaginal exposures in actual setting, with friend or therapist
- Go through same without friend, and then without cell phone
- Have friend drop you off in rural area alone and return in thirty minutes (no cell phone)

USING PUBLIC TRANSPORTATION

Imaginal

- Imagine watching others get on bus or subway
- Imagine walking down into subway station or standing at bus stop. Picture this vividly, including sounds of people nearby, smell of the setting, weather outside, sound of bus or train pulling up
- Walking onto bus/train
- Door closing behind you
- Taking seat or holding overhead rail
- Exiting bus/train
- With subway, picture going above ground then going back underground
- With buses, into tunnel then out again; or over bridges
- Record narration of this imaginal trip for review and practice at home
- View videos of trips on buses or subways

In Vivo

- Follow steps similar to the imaginal items above; may do with therapist or friend first, then alone
- Might add steps such as just waiting at train/bus stop for a time without boarding
- Take short trip to next stop only, then move to longer trips
- Doing without cell phone may increase anxiety and strength of exposure by eliminating safety cue

Response Prevention

- Changing modes of travel to avoid public transportation

OPEN PLACES/PARKING LOTS

Imaginal

- Several items from Being Outside Alone may help
- Imagine getting out of car in own driveway
- Then parking in small strip mall or convenience store when lot is mostly full
- Now same mall but no one else parked there
- Get out of car in busy mall parking lot with people coming and going and most spots filled
- Same mall parking lot early in morning when empty, and walk perimeter of lot
- Or on floor by oneself in parking garage
- View pictures of parking areas at malls or stadiums

In Vivo

- Follow steps in imaginal exposures above, but in real world
- Might add steps for each where person parks car in each setting but does not get out, then later does exposure again while getting out of car and standing near car, then finally walks away from car into building or around circumference of parking lot
- Doing same without cell phone (if this increases anxiety)

- Walk across large athletic field, park, or open meadow

Response Prevention

- Shopping at different stores to avoid large parking lots
- Parking at inconvenient spots to avoid same

SHOPPING MALLS/THEATERS

Imaginal

- Describe to therapist in detail layout of familiar mall if able to do so
- If not, study map of nearby mall
- Look at pictures/video of mall (likely available at mall's website)
- Picture going to mall, initially going into nearby store and walking back out
- Create narrative from leaving home to parking to walking into mall, going through doors, through predetermined route to store at far end of mall, making purchase, stopping to eat at food court, then leaving. Be specific: name store where item purchased and eatery where meal purchased. Be vivid with sounds (people, elevator music), sights (storefronts, ads, kiosks), smells (perfumes, food aromas), touch (door handle, handrail on stairs or escalator, texture of food)
- This might be assisted by friend making video as he walks route that is laid out (making for a semi-VR walk through mall) and viewing this as exposure
- For theater, adapt above to standing in theater lobby, then walking into theater, then standing with lights on, then off, then sitting through entire show/movie

In Vivo

The following steps can be done initially with therapist or friend, then alone.

- Stand outside mall
- Walk into mall and walk around or just stand
- Purchase something in mall
- Work up to accomplishing detailed visit in imaginal exposure in reality

- Ideally, in final exposure client is alone with no therapist or friend even in parking lot and is without cell phone or other communication device
- Similar adaptation for theater exposure as above

Response Prevention

- Avoiding outings with friends to malls and theaters
- Shopping in "safer" places to avoid ones that create anxiety
- Having others do shopping to avoid going to feared locales

STANDING IN LINE OR IN A CROWD

Imaginal

- Picture standing in short line of about three people buying movie tickets
- Imagine standing in line at grocery store and several people line up behind you, with counters on either side boxing you in
- Picture arriving early for concert with doors not open yet and waiting in lobby
- Imagine crowd slowly gathers. Noise increases and people crowd near. Finally it is virtually packed. Doors open and folks push to get into lines to enter concert hall. Do this with venue familiar to client if possible
- Supplement above with photos or videos of theater
- Do similar imaginal exposure with buying token for subway
- Watch videos of crowds moving toward door and track individuals in them rather than just "big picture"

In Vivo

- Steps similar to imaginal ones above
- Add graded exposures as needed, with friend or therapist first, then alone, such as...
    - Buying movie ticket with no one in line
    - Getting in queue at fast-food restaurant with rails to guide queue. Do first with no one in line, then at a busy time where people are in front of and behind you

- Attend sports event or concert at large venue

Response Prevention

- Avoiding restaurants with lines, with waiting lists, or that are loud and crowded
- Changing times to go places so as to avoid anxiety associated with crowds
- Not going to entertainment events due to crowds

CHAPTER 13

Exposure Therapy for Obsessive-Compulsive Disorder, Generalized Anxiety Disorder, and Hypochondriasis

Obsessive-compulsive disorder (OCD) is characterized by thoughts that become "stuck" in the brain and can be unrelenting, varying from worries to intrusive thoughts of violence, sexuality, or blasphemy. Compulsions typically are the actions taken to temporarily relieve the anxiety associated with the obsessions. Obsessive-compulsive disorder may even have its own group of disorders in DSM-5 (American Psychiatric Association, 2012), which is currently in development. This group may include body dysmorphic disorder, hoarding, hair-pulling, skin-picking, and similar disorders. Generalized anxiety disorder (GAD) is one of these as it is characterized by intrusive thoughts, albeit of a different type than OCD. Generalized anxiety disorder is characterized by worrying (American Psychiatric Association, 2012) that is persistent and out of proportion to the actual concern being worried about.

What has been called "hypochondriasis" is also typified by worry, in this case about health-related matters. Proposed changes in DSM-5 (American Psychiatric Association, 2012) would create a new category of disorder called complex somatic symptom disorder (CSSD), which is characterized by excessive thoughts, feelings, and behaviors related to somatic symptoms or health concerns. Specific manifestations of CSSD include predominant somatic complaints (formerly somatization disorder), predominant pain (formerly pain disorder), and predominant health anxiety, the new name for hypochondriasis. As it involves anxiety, it can be treated with exposure therapy. In this chapter we will note how each of these disorders can be addressed by forms of ET.

While the mechanisms for exposure therapy and response prevention are sometimes different when working with OCD, exposure-based therapy is still the most effective psychological treatment for this disorder (Abramowitz & Larsen, 2007). In many cases, the use is similar to what we have already covered. For example, in the case of a person who is obsessed with germs, the therapist will expose him to places avoided due to alleged germs. Response prevention will focus on preventing the person from performing a ritual to reduce the obsession (such as washing hands), which negatively reinforces the obsession and worsens it even as it provides very temporary relief.

However, the DSM does not require both obsessions and compulsions to be present, and some of the most challenging variants of OCD are the ones with intrusive thoughts that create anxiety but are not necessarily associated with compulsions. This requires exposure to address the thoughts but no "real world" situations. This amounts to mental exposure to the anxiety without environmental exposure to a feared situation. This can be effective (Thyer, 1985) but entails exposing the client to her own anxious thoughts without her trying to avoid or escape them. Good summaries of detailed adaptations of exposure and response prevention for OCD can be found in Rowa, Antony, and Swinson (2007) and Abramowitz and Larsen (2007). In this chapter, obsessive, intrusive thoughts are their own category, followed by common obsessions that are more amenable to external exposure, noting response prevention ideas along the way. Note, too, that many obsessions are related to fears covered elsewhere in Part II of this book. We then conclude with some suggestions for several of the OCD-related disorders.

The worries of GAD can be treated much like the intrusive thoughts of OCD. These thoughts differ in that they are more "obsessions" about the "what ifs" of future possibilities than vile or troublesome thoughts or impulses to do something offensive to the thinker. Worries are preoccupations with avoiding negative outcomes that are highly improbable, aimed at finding a certain plan of prevention that will serve to reduce the anxious arousal of the worrying process. It is, in a way, obsessing with no compulsion to provide immediate (and very temporary) relief. Generalized anxiety disorder is marked by an intolerance of uncertainty (Dugas et al., 2003). As such, it is likely amenable to ACT, but has most often been treated through CBT (Dugas & Robichaud, 2007).

Dugas and Robichaud (2007) recommend imaginal (sometimes called "cognitive") exposure for GAD. One sets up the exposure by using the downward arrow technique of asking "what would happen next?" until reaching the most dire result that could come from the worry. A scenario is then developed to imagine this happening. This can be recorded and listened to repeatedly as an exposure. Dugas et al. (2003) demonstrated that this can even be effective in group therapy for GAD. Another variant that may prove helpful is to create a hierarchy of distressing scenes based on distressing images, thoughts, or scenes associated with the worries, confronting each in turn through exposure (Abramowitz et al., 2011).

Treatment of the predominant health anxiety form of CSSD may follow closely a model of treating OCD (Himle & Hoffman, 2007). One might begin with CBT for the "obsessive" thoughts about health, but then add exposures as needed. Response prevention serves a similar function here as in OCD by preventing behaviors that seek to artificially alleviate the distress of the health fear.

Exposure Ideas for OCD

INTRUSIVE THOUGHTS (AGGRESSION, BLASPHEMY, SEXUAL THOUGHTS)

The suggestions in this section can be applied across all thoughts in this category and may apply to worries as well.

Imaginal

- Picture feared outcome from having thoughts (if thoughts are of doing something harmful or sexual)

In Vivo

- Write down all the intrusive thoughts*
- Read thoughts out loud*
- Make audio recording of thoughts and listen to it ten times daily*
- Listen to it particularly in contexts that trigger the thoughts**
- Acknowledge thoughts while attributing them to OCD rather than self
- Relate thoughts to therapist as they come, without attempting to escape or debate
- Use mindfulness and acceptance approaches to thoughts

(Items with * adapted from Thyer, 1985; with ** adapted from Abramowitz et al., 2011)

Response Prevention

- Debating thoughts or trying to prove they are not accurate
- If blasphemous thoughts, asking God for forgiveness or confessing to others
- Asking others for reassurance or comfort
- Avoiding situations/contexts that tend to trigger thoughts
- Counting compulsively to relieve anxiety caused by thoughts
- Accompanying thoughts with mental rituals

CONTAMINATION/GERMS

Imaginal

- Picture someone coughing next to you on crowded bus
- A mussed-up construction worker with greasy hands getting silverware from the dispenser just before you do at self-serve restaurant (customize similar scenarios to client's needs)
- Imagine germs crawling on door handle, floating in air
- Imagine germs flowing up nose and beginning to reproduce
- Visualize worst-case scenario re: germs or contamination
- Look at pictures and/or videos of germs under microscope
- Watch videos of people living in very unsanitary conditions

In Vivo

- Contaminate paper towel with bathroom germs and practice touching towel*
- Touch doorknobs, faucets, toilet seats, floor near urinals*
- Rub hand in dirt and do not wash
- Eat food that has been on floor*
- Pick up trash on street and put in garbage can
- Eat meal without washing hands before
- Touch greasy engine (while cold, of course)
- Eat apple without washing it first
- Sit in doctor's waiting area for patients who are not contagious
- Visit someone in hospital
- Ride on crowded bus or train

(Items with * adapted from Abramowitz et al., 2011)

Response Prevention

- Avoiding places that might have germs

- Not eating certain foods for fear of germs
- Washing hands excessively (either for too long or too often)
- Showering/bathing for too long or too often
- Carrying and/or using hand sanitizer or sanitary wipes excessively
- Washing and cleaning excessively

HARMING SELF/OTHERS ACCIDENTALLY OR INTENTIONALLY

Imaginal

- Visualize dreaded harm actually occurring (for example, hitting pedestrian while driving, hitting friend, pushing person into traffic, burning down house due to leaving coffee pot on, house being robbed and vandalized due to leaving it unlocked).
- Do this in detail while engaging multiple senses and following narrative through any consequences that follow (such as lawsuit, arrest, dealing with insurance company).

In Vivo

- With permission, ask friend to allow you to pretend to hit her
- Intentionally leave coffee pot on while out of house for a period of time
- Leave window unlocked while out of house for a while (if it is safe to do so where you live)
- Place traffic cone or other object on curb in neighborhood and intentionally hit it while driving

Response Prevention

- Engaging in irrational repetitive behaviors (knocking on wall five times, closing door three times) or magical rituals (only driving on certain streets)
- Engaging in directly associated compulsions, including checking (to see if coffee pot is off, for example)
- Staring at hair dryer, coffee pot, stove, and so on
- Other rituals to check/prevent harm

SYMMETRY/DISORDER

Imaginal

- Visualize a room or other setting with things in disarray. Be very specific to include things that bother you
- Imagine sitting in this place and being mindful of asymmetries without trying to change them

In Vivo

- For counting obsessions, deliberately count to number other than that required by the obsession
- Resist impulse to change things that are out of line or order (for example, if someone else puts magazines, dishes, or tools in different place or order)
- Deliberately cause disorder by moving things, changing an order, or having a number of items that varies from the obsessional number
- Mess up arrangement of socks (for example) in dresser drawers
- Step on sidewalk cracks
- For repetitive behaviors (such as tapping), do "wrong" number of times (not number that brings relief)
- Refuse to count steps when walking or count items
- Misspell a word on purpose when writing, or intentionally do not use best handwriting

Response Prevention

- Using any rituals, counting, or actions to create symmetry associated with obsession with things being "just right"
- Actively avoiding things that are asymmetrical

TEXTURES (FOOD, CLOTHING, AND SO ON)

Imaginal

- Imagine day at work with clothing tag itching

- Clothes too tight or too loose
- Wearing itchy sweater
- Wearing different clothes from those that make you feel okay
- Slowly chewing food with annoying texture
- Viewing pictures of textures that trouble you

In Vivo

- Touch pieces of cloth with unpleasant textures
- Eat foods with bothersome textures
- Do imaginal exposures in actual life (for example, put itchy tag in neck of shirt or blouse)
- Have someone else pick out meal items and clothing

Response Prevention

- Any avoidance of contact with items that make you uncomfortable
- Wearing same underwear or clothes in same pattern

HOARDING

Imaginal

Key to exposure in hoarding is restructuring beliefs around hoarding, and this is key for success with any exposure here.*

- Visualize house with hoarded items gone
- Imagine seeing an item typically hoarded and passing by without keeping it. Incorporate places where such items are often encountered
- Imagine as reality the outcome feared if you did not hoard*
- Specifically, imagine losing information if newspapers or other things were discarded*
- Imagine consequences of discarding (this is step toward making subjective decision to discard)*

In Vivo

Much hoarding is a way to avoid making decisions, so decisions can be a form of exposure.*

- Make decisions about limiting how clutter comes into the house (get off mailing lists; subscribe to online newspaper rather than paper one)*
- Decide where discarded clutter will go*
- Decide to discard one item and then do so*
- Discard certain percentage of clutter
- Increase percentage

Response Prevention

- Avoiding noticing clutter (if hoarding behavior involves ignoring clutter)*
- Keeping clutter in sight (if hoarding behavior is related to fear of losing or forgetting)*
- Going places or doing things to get items that are hoarded

(Items marked with * adapted from Cherian & Frost, 2007)

COMPULSIVE BEHAVIORS (HAIR PULLING, SKIN PICKING)

Imaginal

Exposure with these more often involves exposure to the anxious feeling of *not* engaging in the behavior.

- Visualize self in situations where behavior is common, while feeling urge to do behavior but resisting

In Vivo

- Put hand in actual position of doing the behavior (hold hair in hand but don't pull; put fingernail to place where you often pick) and hold position while impulse fades
- Practice same in settings where behavior is common (watching television, going to sleep)
- For skin picking, rub white glue on fingertips and allow to dry to simulate urge to pick skin. Wash off rather than peel

Response Prevention

- Avoiding incompatible behaviors (RP would incorporate these, for example: playing with putty or paper clip, wearing gloves or shower cap to bed to avoid hair pulling, putting tight bandage over areas often picked)

Worries

Remember, these exposures are best if directly related to the client's specific worries. May be graded from easy to difficult, ending with worst-case scenario in a narrative form with multisensory details.

MONEY

Imaginal

- Having identity stolen and bank accounts drained while credit cards maxed out
- Severe damage to house in storm and insurance company refuses to pay
- Investments all lost to embezzling broker who leaves town
- Going to pay at restaurant with no cash or credit cards
- Credit card rejected at retail store

In Vivo

- Go to mall intentionally without any money or credit cards

Response Prevention

- Checking bank account
- Counting money in wallet
- Calculating budget excessively

ONE'S CHILDREN

Imaginal

- Child becomes sick and dies

- Child rebels against parent's values (runs away, gets pregnant, becomes heavy drug user)
- Child is in accident at school and taken to emergency room
- Teenager totals car in accident
- Child fails all classes; announces refusal to go to college or decision to drop out of school

Response Prevention

- Excessive texting/calling child when away from home, or requiring child to check in more than really needed
- Preventing child from taking normal risks for age
- Seeking reassurance from partner regarding child

RELATIONSHIPS

Imaginal

- Partner has affair and leaves
- Partner does not come home on time and will not say where he was
- Friend does not call or text for extended period of time without giving reason
- Learn everyone at work had party and did not invite you
- Being "unfriended" on social networking sites by several people at once without reason

In Vivo

- Have partner agree to come home late sometime soon but not say when
- Have friend agree to no contact for period of time
- Stay away from social networking sites for period of time

Response Prevention

- Frequently checking cell phone or social networking sites (RP could include turning off checking features of cell phone and checking only on set schedule)
- Calling or checking in with others excessively

- Seeking reassurance about relationship with another person

JOB SECURITY

Imaginal

- Getting poor performance review
- Learning others got raise and you didn't
- Hearing rumor of upcoming layoffs
- Getting passed over for promotion
- Boss asks to meet you and no reason given
- Being blamed for foul-up at work that was your responsibility
- Suddenly being fired without reason

Response Prevention

- Reassurance seeking from colleagues and superiors
- Looking for job openings "just in case"
- Planning for job loss though there are no objective signs this is imminent
- Working too hard or not speaking up to protect job

SAFETY

Imaginal

- Stumbling down steps
- Having fender bender
- Developing appendicitis and having to go to hospital for surgery
- Having serious auto accident that is not your fault
- Having serious auto accident that is your fault
- Slipping with saw and cutting finger

- Having serious injury and going on disability; loved one having to help you with basic needs

In Vivo

- Do things that one worries might lead to injury (so long as the worry is truly irrational)

Response Prevention

- Avoiding chores and responsibilities due to worry about getting hurt
- Excessively planning activities to avoid injury/accident
- Refusing pleasurable activities because of worry about accidents

DEATH

Imaginal

- Picture going to funeral of another
- Picture various scenarios of how one might die:
    - Sudden accident
    - Chronic illness
    - Cancer
    - After living several years in nursing home
    - Include impact on family, friends, workplace
- Imagine own funeral

In Vivo

- Strongly discouraged ☺ (though attending funeral or visiting cemetery is an option).

Response Prevention

- Making undue plans for one's passing (excessively reviewing wills, double-checking insurance policies)
- Asking for reassurance or guidance about how to live longer

- Avoiding funerals you ought to attend

Health Anxiety (Hypochondriasis)

Imaginal

- Some items under Obsession with Contamination/Germs above may be relevant
- Reading about feared disease
- Watching videos or movies depicting feared disease
- Child comes home with contagious disease client has not had
- Sitting in waiting room at emergency room and hearing others cough, moan, vomit
- Having moles on body that doctor is unsure about
- After tests, doctor says this is skin cancer and surgery is required
- Similar with internal form of cancer (for example, finding a lump in breast or abdomen)
- Having headaches with no known cause
- Feeling faint
- Feeling nauseous
- Being hospitalized (be detailed in making this realistic)
- Being diagnosed with tuberculosis or other feared disease
- Create narrative of worst-case scenario of most feared illnesses

Interoceptive

- See suggestions in Chapter 12

In Vivo

- Raise eyebrows high and hold until pain or strange sensation in head results
- Sit still, be quiet, and observe all normal sensations, tensions, and even pain that are generally overlooked

- Visit waiting area of emergency room
- Visit others in hospital

Response Prevention

- Making unnecessary doctor appointments
- Researching symptoms in books or on Internet
- Watching health programs on television
- Taking unneeded food supplements
- Taking excessive pain relievers/antacids

CHAPTER 14

Suggestions for Emotion Exposure

In Chapter 8, emotion exposure was discussed as a helpful tool for problems beyond anxiety. Review that section for more on how to use exposure and response prevention with other emotions. We conclude our study of exposure by positing some suggestions for exposure for emotions other than anxiety—this is an area that will expand in the years to come. These exposures are typically incorporated into hierarchies. Further details on ways to use emotion exposure are found in McKay, Fanning, and Ona (2011) (this is the source for all items in this chapter marked with *).

Depression/Sadness

A variety of activities become unpleasant when one is depressed, and enduring the unpleasantness of being active can be a form of exposure. One may also sit with thoughts and images that evoke the depressed feeling. Here are a few examples.

Imaginal

- Recall failures in life*
- Keep negative thoughts (such as "I'm pitiful" or "I'm no good") in mind
- Imagine coworker complaining about you to someone else
- And then to your face
- Imagine worst-case scenario for your future*
- Recall painful losses (pet dying, and so on)*
- Imagine painful losses that might occur*

Interoceptive

- Hold head down*
- Tense major muscle groups and hold*
- Tighten jaw; frown*
- Carry ten-pound weight around*

In Vivo

- Any number of activities that move client from inertia
- Go for walk
- Do dishes or other chores*
- Go out to eat
- Call someone to talk
- Speak to coworker or neighbor you think doesn't like you
- Do something fun such as go to movies or sports event

Response Prevention

- Avoiding social contact*
- Avoiding activities or chores
- Withdrawing*
- Sleeping excessively*
- Using drugs or alcohol*
- Ruminating about past or potential failures*
- Sitting on couch and not moving*

Anger

Imaginal

- Think of unfair things in society or the news*
- Watch videos or movies depicting injustice or people who are angry
- Recall things done wrong to you
- Imagine irritating things being done to you (neighbor breaks your window; catching coworker gossiping about you; pet tears up something in the house; child making noise or refusing to obey)
- Imagine being stuck in traffic
- Imagine arguing with person you don't like

Interoceptive

- Many exercises for shortness of breath, heart palpitations in Chapter 12 can be useful to simulate feeling of anger
- Sit near heater to create hot feeling of being angry
- Run in heavy clothes to create overheated feeling*

In Vivo

- Sit in traffic jam
- Listen to politician with whom you disagree
- Listen to music of a genre you hate
- Discuss controversial subject with friend who agrees to debate at every point

Response Prevention

- Being aggressive verbally or physically*
- Using alcohol or drugs*
- Ruminating about irritating events*
- "Venting" anger by hitting things, tearing things up, and so on

Shame

Imaginal

- Picture entering nice restaurant with fly unzipped, or wearing jeans at fancy restaurant
- Being on stage in play and forgetting lines
- Boss tells you that you forgot to show up for your shift
- Friend comments that you look sick or homely or out of style
- Recall topics that make you feel ashamed
- Recount events where you felt shamed

Interoceptive

- See suggestions for panic disorder in Chapter 12 and under Depression/Sadness above, as either of those might capture sensations of being ashamed

In Vivo

- Purposefully go out dressed too casually for formal place, or too formally for casual place. or with mismatched clothes
- Go out without makeup or with hair mussed
- Go to sporting event wearing gear for opposing team
- Sing karaoke and mess up intentionally
- Do something you think is "shameful" like not leaving tip at restaurant or leaving trash on table at fast-food restaurant
- Ask friend to occasionally say something to you that you feel is shaming you
- Show up for work late (if it is reasonable to do so)

Response Prevention

- Avoiding places, situations, or people associated with feeling ashamed*
- Withdrawing or shutting down*
- Ruminating about past shameful situations in hopes of finding something redeeming*
- Using anger to suppress shame*
- Avoiding activities for fear you might feel ashamed

References

Abramowitz, J. S., Deacon, B. J., & Whiteside, S. P. H. (2011). *Exposure therapy for anxiety: Principles and practice.* New York: Guilford.

Abramowitz, J. S., & Larsen, K. E. (2007). Exposure therapy for obsessive-compulsive disorder. In D. C. S. Richard & D. L. Lauterbach (Eds.), *Handbook of exposure therapies* (pp. 185–208). Boston: Academic Press.

Abramowitz, J. S., Whiteside, S., Kalsy, S. A., & Tolin, D. F. (2003). Thought control strategies in obsessive-compulsive disorder: A replication and extension. *Behaviour Research and Therapy, 41,* 529–540.

American Psychiatric Association. (2000). *Diagnostic and statistical manual* (4th ed., Text Revision). Washington, DC: Author.

American Psychiatric Association (2012). *DSM-5 development.* Retrieved from http://www.dsm5.org

Anderson, P., Rothbaum, B. O., & Hodges, L. F. (2003). Virtual reality exposure in the treatment of social anxiety. *Cognitive and Behavioral Practice, 10,* 240–247.

Andersson, G., Waara, J., Jonsson, U., Fredrik, M., Carlbring, P., & Lars-Göran, O. (2009). Internet-based self-help versus one-session exposure in the treatment of spider phobia: A randomized controlled trial. *Cognitive Behaviour Therapy, 38,* 114–120. doi: 10.1080/16506070902931326

Antony, M. M. (2011). Recent advances in the treatment of anxiety disorders. *Canadian Psychology, 52,* 1–9. doi: 10.1037/a022237

Antony, M. M., & Swinson, R. P. (2000). *Phobic disorders and panic in adults: A guide to assessment and treatment.* Washington, DC: American Psychological Association.

Barlow, D. H. (2002). *Anxiety and its disorders: The nature and treatment of anxiety and panic* (2nd ed.). New York: Guilford.

Barlow, D. H., Allen, L. B., & Choate, M. L. (2004). Toward a unified treatment for emotional disorders. *Behavior Therapy, 35,* 205–230.

Barlow, D. H., Ellard, K. K., Fairholme, C. P., Farchione, T. J., Boisseau, C. L., Ehrenreich-May, J. T., & Allen, L. B. (2010). *Unified protocol for transdiagnostic treatment of emotional disorders: Workbook.* New York: Oxford University Press.

Barlow, D. H., Farchione, T. J., Fairholme, C. P., Ellard, K. K., Boisseau, C. L., Allen, L. B., & Ehrenreich-May, J. (2011). *Unified protocol for transdiagnostic treatment of emotional disorders: Therapist guide.* New York: Oxford University Press.

Barlow, D. H., Raffa, S. D., & Cohen, E. M. (2002). Psychosocial treatments for panic disorders, phobias, and generalized anxiety disorder. In P. E. Nathan & J. M. Gorman (Eds.), *A guide to treatments that work* (2nd ed., pp. 301–335). New York: Oxford University Press.

Batten, S. V. (2011). *Essentials of acceptance and commitment therapy*. Los Angeles: Sage Publications.

Beck, A. T. (1979). *Cognitive therapy for the emotional disorders*. New York: International Universities Press.

Beck, A. T., & Steer, R. A. (1990). *Manual for the Beck Anxiety Inventory*. San Antonio, TX: Psychological Corporation.

Beck, J. (2011). *Cognitive behavior therapy: Basics and beyond* (2nd ed.). New York: Guilford.

Becker, C. B., Darius, E., & Schaumberg, K. (2007). An analog study of patient preferences for exposure versus alternative treatments for posttraumatic stress disorder. *Behaviour Research and Therapy, 45*, 2861–2873.

Becker, C. B., & Zayfert, C. (2001). Integrating DBT-based techniques and concepts to facilitate exposure treatment for PTSD. *Cognitive and Behavioral Practice, 8*, 107–122.

Becker, C. B., Zayfert, C., & Anderson, E. (2004). A survey of psychologists' attitudes towards and utilization of exposure therapy for PTSD. *Behaviour Research and Therapy, 42*, 277–292. doi: 10.1016/S0005-7967(03)00138-4

Bögels, S. M., Alden, L., Beidel, D. C., Clark, L. A., Pine, D. S., Stein, M. B., & Voncken, M. (2010). Social anxiety disorder: Questions and answers for the DSM-V. *Depression and Anxiety, 27*, 168–189.

Bouchard, S., Côté, S., & Richard, D. C. S. (2007). Virtual reality applications for exposure. In D. C. S. Richard & D. L. Lauterbach (Eds.), *Handbook of exposure therapies* (pp. 347–388). Boston: Academic Press.

Britton, J. C., Lissek, S., Grillon, C., Norcross, M. A., & Pine, D. S. (2011). Development of anxiety: The role of threat appraisal and fear learning. *Depression and Anxiety, 28*, 5–17.

Brown, T. A., Campbell, A., Lehman, C. L., Grisham, J. R., & Mancill, R. B. (2001). Current and lifetime comorbidity of the DSM-IV anxiety and mood disorders in a large clinical sample. *Journal of Abnormal Psychology, 110*, 49–58.

Burijon, B. N. (2007). *Biological bases of clinical anxiety*. New York: W. W. Norton.

Butler, G., Fennell, M., & Hackmann, A. (2008). *Cognitive-behavioral therapy for anxiety disorders: Mastering clinical challenges*. New York: Guilford.

Cahill, S. P., Rothbaum, B. O., Resick, P. A., & Follette, V. M. (2009). Cognitive behavior therapy for adults. In E. B. Foa, T. M. Keane, M. J. Friedman, & J. A. Cohen (Eds.), *Effective treatments for PTSD: Practice guidelines from the International Society for Traumatic Stress Studies* (pp. 138–222). New York: Guilford.

Cherian, A. E., & Frost, R. O. (2007). Treating compulsive hoarding. In M. M. Antony, C. Purdon, & L. J. Summerfeldt (Eds.), *Psychological treatment of obsessive-compulsive disorder: Fundamentals and beyond* (pp. 231–249). Washington, DC: American Psychological Association.

Chorpita, B. F. (2007). *Modular cognitive-behavioral therapy for childhood anxiety disorders*. New York: Guilford.

Chrestman, K. R., Gilboa-Schechtman, E., & Foa, E. B. (2008). *Prolonged exposure therapy for PTSD: Teen workbook*. New York: Oxford University Press.

Clark, D. A., & Beck, A. T. (2010). *Cognitive therapy of anxiety disorders: Science and practice*. New York: Guilford.

Craske, M. G., & Barlow, D. H. (2001). Panic disorder and agoraphobia. In D. H. Barlow (Ed.), *Clinical handbook of psychological disorders* (3rd ed., pp. 1–59). New York: Guilford.

Davison, G. C. (1968). Systematic desensitization as a counterconditioning process. *Journal of Abnormal Psychology, 73*, 91–99.

Dimidjian, S., Hollon, S. D., Dobson, S. D., Schamling, K. B., Kohlenberg, R. J.,…Jacobson, N. S. (2006). Randomized trial of behavioral activation, cognitive therapy, and antidepressant medication in acute treatment of adults with major depression. *Journal of Consulting and Clinical Psychology, 74*, 658–670.

Dobson, D., & Dobson, K. S. (2009). *Evidence-based practice of cognitive-behavioral therapy.* New York: Guilford.

Dobson, K. S., & Dozois, D. J. A. (2001). Historical and philosophical bases of the cognitive-behavioral therapies. In K. S. Dobson (Ed.), *Handbook of cognitive-behavioral therapies* (2nd ed., pp. 3–39). New York: Guilford.

Dougherty, D. D., Rauch, S. L., & Jenike, M. A. (2002). Pharmacological treatments for obsessive compulsive disorder. In P. E. Nathan & J. M. Gorman (Eds.), *A guide to treatments that work* (2nd ed., pp. 387–410). New York: Oxford University Press.

Dugas, M. J., Ladouceur, R., Léger, E., Freeston, M. H., Langlois, F., Provencher, M. D., & Boisvert, J. (2003). Group cognitive-behavioral therapy for generalized anxiety disorder: Treatment outcome and long-term follow-up. *Journal of Consulting and Clinical Psychology, 71*, 821–825. doi: 10.10337/0022-006X.71.4.821

Dugas, M. J., & Robichaud, M. (2007). *Cognitive-behavioral treatment for generalized anxiety disorder.* New York: Routledge.

Eifert, G. H., & Forsyth, J. P. (2005). *Acceptance and commitment therapy for anxiety disorders: A practitioner's guide to using mindfulness, acceptance, and values-based behavior change strategies.* Oakland, CA: New Harbinger.

Ellis, A., & Blau, S. (1998). (Eds.). *The Albert Ellis reader: A guide to well-being using rational-emotive behavior therapy.* New York: Citadel Press.

Fisher, J. E., & O'Donohue, W. T. (Eds.). (2006). *Practitioner's guide to evidence-based therapy.* New York: Springer.

Foa, E. B. (2011). Prolonged exposure therapy: Past, present, and future. *Depression and Anxiety, 28*, 1043–1047.

Foa, E. B., & Cahill, S. P. (2001). Psychological therapies: Emotional processing. In N. J. Smelser & P. B. Bates (Eds.), *International encyclopedia of the social and behavioral sciences* (pp. 12363–12369). Oxford: Elsevier.

Foa, E. B., Hembree, E. A., Cahill, S. P., Rauch, S. A., Riggs, D. S., Feeny, N. C., & Yadin, E. (2005). Randomized trial of prolonged exposure for PTSD with and without cognitive restructuring: Outcome at academic and community clinics. *Journal of Consulting and Clinical Psychology, 73*, 953–964.

Foa, E. B., Hembree, E. A., & Rothbaum, B. O. (2007). *Prolonged exposure therapy for PTSD: Emotional processing of traumatic experiences, Therapist Guide.* New York: Oxford University Press.

Foa, E. B., Huppert, J. D., & Cahill, S. P. (2006). Emotional processing theory: An update. In B. O. Rothbaum (Ed.), *Pathological anxiety: Emotional processing in etiology and treatment* (pp. 3–24). New York: Guilford.

Foa, E. B., & Kozak, M. J. (1985). Treatment of anxiety disorders: Implications for psychopathology. In A. H. Tuma & J. Maser (Eds.), *Anxiety and the anxiety disorders* (pp. 421–461). Hillsdale, NJ: Erlbaum.

Foa, E. B., & Kozak, M. J. (1986). Emotional processing of fear: Exposure to corrective information. *Psychological Bulletin, 99*, 20–35.

Foa, E. B., Steketee, G., Grayson, J. B., Turner, R. M., & Latimer, P. (1984). Deliberate exposure and blocking of obsessive-compulsive rituals: Immediate and long-term effects. *Behavior Therapy, 15*, 450–472.

Forsyth, J. P., Barrios, V., & Acheson, D. T. (2007). Exposure therapy and cognitive interventions for the anxiety disorders: Overview and newer third-generation perspectives. In D. C. S. Richard & D. L. Lauterbach (Eds.), *Handbook of exposure therapies* (pp. 61–108). Boston: Academic Press.

Forsyth, J. P., & Eifert, G. H. (2007). *The mindfulness & acceptance workbook for anxiety: A guide to breaking free from anxiety, phobias & worry using acceptance & commitment therapy*. Oakland, CA: New Harbinger.

Forsyth, J. P., Fusé, T., & Acheson, D. T. (2008). Interoceptive exposure for panic disorder. In W. T. O'Donohue & J. E. Fisher (Eds.), *Cognitive behavior therapy: Applying empirically supported techniques in your practice* (pp. 296–308). New York: Wiley.

Franklin, M. E., Abramowitz, J. S., Kozak, M. J., Levitt, J. T., & Foa, E. B. (2000). Effectiveness of exposure and ritual prevention for obsessive-compulsive disorder: Randomized compared with nonrandomized samples. *Journal of Consulting and Clinical Psychology, 68*, 594–602.

Franklin, M. E., & Foa, E. B. (2002). Cognitive behavioral treatment of obsessive-compulsive disorder. In P. E. Nathan & J. M. Gorman (Eds.), *A guide to treatments that work* (2nd ed., pp. 431–446). New York: Oxford University Press.

Franklin, M. E., Ledley, D. A. & Foa, E. B. (2008). Response prevention. In W. T. O'Donohue & J. E. Fisher (Eds.), *Cognitive behavior therapy: Applying empirically supported techniques in your practice* (pp. 445–451). New York: Wiley.

Freud, S. (1909/1955). Analysis of a five-year-old boy. In J. Strachey (Ed. & Trans.). *The standard edition of the complete psychological works of Sigmund Freud.* (Vol. 10, pp. 3–149). London: Hogarth Press.

Freud, S. (1920/1966). *Introductory lectures on psychoanalysis.* New York: W. W. Norton.

Ghosh, A., & Marks, I. M. (1987). Self-treatment of agoraphobia by exposure. *Behavior Therapy, 18*, 3–16.

Gibson, E. J., & Walk, R. D. (1960). The "visual cliff." *Scientific American, 202*, 64–71.

Gortner, E.-M., Rude, S. S., & Pennebaker, J. W. (2006). Benefits of expressive writing in lowering rumination and depressive symptoms. *Behavior Therapy, 37*, 292–303.

Götestam, K. G., & Svebak, S. (2009). Treatment of tunnel phobia: An experimental field study. *Cognitive Behaviour Therapy, 38*, 146–152. doi: 10.1080/16506070802675262

Grunes, M. S., Neziroglu, F., & McKay, D. (2001). Family involvement in the behavioral treatment of obsessive-compulsive disorder: A preliminary investigation. *Behavior Therapy, 32*, 803–820.

Harman, J. S., Rollman, B. L., Hanusa, B. H., Lenze, E. J., & Shear, M. K. (2002). Physician office visits of adults for anxiety disorders in the United States, 1985–1998. *Journal of General Internal Medicine, 17*, 165–172.

Harris, S. R., Kemmerling, R. L., & North, M. M. (2002). Brief virtual reality therapy for public speaking anxiety. *Cyberpsychology and Behavior, 5*, 543–550.

Hayes, A. M., Beevers, C. G., Feldman, G. C., Laurenceau, J-P., & Perlman, C. (2005). Avoidance and processing as predictors of symptom change and positive growth in an integrative therapy for depression. *International Journal of Behavioral Medicine, 12*, 111–122.

Hayes, A. M., Feldman, G. C., Beevers, C. G., Laurenceau, J.-P., Cardaciotto, L., & Lewis-Smith, J. (2007). Discontinuities and cognitive changes in an exposure-based cognitive therapy for depression. *Journal of Consulting and Clinical Psychology, 75*, 409–421. doi: 10.1037/0022-006X.75.3.409

Hayes, A. M., & Harris, M. S. (2000). The development of an integrative treatment for depression. In S. Johnson, A. M. Hayes, T. Field, N. Schneiderman, & P. McCabe (Eds.), *Stress, coping and depression* (pp. 291–306). Mahwah, NJ: Erlbaum.

Hayes, S. C. (2005). Foreword. In G. H. Eifert & J. P. Forsyth, *Acceptance and commitment therapy: A practitioner's treatment guide to using mindfulness, acceptance, and values-based behavior change strategies* (pp. v–vii). Oakland, CA: New Harbinger.

Hayes, S. C., Barnes-Holmes, D., & Roche, B. (2001). *Relational frame theory: A post-Skinnerian account of human language and cognition.* New York: Plenum Press.

Hayes, S. C., Strosahl, K. D., & Wilson, K. G. (2011). *Acceptance and commitment therapy: The process and practice of mindful change* (2nd ed.). New York: Guilford.

Hayes, S. C., Strosahl, K. D., & Wilson, K. G. (1999). *Acceptance and commitment therapy: An experiential approach to behavior change.* New York: Guilford.

Hazlett-Stevens, H., & Craske, M. G., (2008). Live (in vivo) exposure. In W. T. O'Donohue & J. E. Fisher (Eds.), *Cognitive behavior therapy: Applying empirically supported techniques in your practice* (pp. 309–316). New York: Wiley.

Head, L. S., & Gross, A. M. (2008). Systematic desensitization. In W. T. O'Donohue & J. E. Fisher (Eds.), *Cognitive behavior therapy: Applying empirically supported techniques in your practice* (pp. 542–549). New York: Wiley.

Herman, J. L. (1992). Complex PTSD: A syndrome in survivors of prolonged and repeated trauma. *Journal of Traumatic Stress, 5*, 377–391.

Himle, J. A., & Hoffman, J. (2007). Exposure therapy for hypochondriasis. In D. C. S. Richard & D. L. Lauterbach (Eds.), *Handbook of exposure therapies* (pp. 299–309). Boston: Academic Press.

Hofmann, S. G., & Barlow, D. H. (2002). Social phobia (social anxiety disorder). In D. H. Barlow (Ed.), *Anxiety and its disorders: The nature and treatment of anxiety and panic* (pp. 454–476). New York: Guilford.

Hoodin, F., & Gillis, G. (2007). Applications of exposure techniques in behavioral medicine. In D. C. S. Richard & D. L. Lauterbach (Eds.), *Handbook of exposure therapies* (pp. 271–298). Boston: Academic Press.

Kagan, J., & Snidman, N. (1991). Infant predictors of inhibited and uninhibited behavioral profiles. *Psychological Science, 2*, 40–44.

Karekla, M., Forsyth, J. P., & Kelly, M. M. (2004). Emotional avoidance and panicogenic responding to a biological challenge procedure. *Behavior Therapy, 35*, 725–746.

Kass, W., & Gilner, F. H. (1974). Drive level, incentive conditions and systematic desensitization. *Behaviour Research and Therapy, 12*, 99–106.

Kessler, R. C., Chiu, W. T., Demler, O., & Walters, E. E. (2005). Prevalence, severity, and comorbidity of 12-month DSM-IV disorders in the National Comorbidity Survey Replication. *Archives of General Psychiatry, 62*, 617–627.

Koch, E. I., Gloster, A. T., & Waller, S. A. (2007). Exposure treatments for panic disorder with and without agoraphobia. In D. C. S. Richard & D. L. Lauterbach (Eds.), *Handbook of exposure therapies* (pp. 221–245). Boston: Academic Press.

Koerner, K., & Dimeff, L. A. (2007). Overview of dialectical behavior therapy. In L. A. Dimeff, & K. Koerner (Eds.), *Dialectical behavior therapy in clinical practice: Applications across disorders and settings* (pp. 1–18). New York: Guilford.

Krijn, M., Emmelkamp, P. M. G., Olafsson, R. O., & Beimond, R. (2004). Virtual reality exposure therapy of anxiety disorders: A review. *Clinical Psychology Review, 24*, 259–281.

Kumar, S., Feldman, G., & Hayes, A. (2008). Changes in mindfulness and emotion regulation in an exposure-based cognitive therapy for depression. *Cognitive Therapy & Research, 32*, 734–744. doi: 10.1007/s10608-008-9190-1

Levis, D. J. (2002). Implosive therapy. In M. Hersen & W. Sledge (Eds.), *Encyclopedia of psychotherapy* (Vol. 2, pp. 1–6). New York: Elsevier Science.

Levis, D. J. (2008). The prolonged CS exposure techniques of implosive (flooding) therapy. In W. T. O'Donohue & J. E. Fisher (Eds.), *Cognitive behavior therapy: Applying empirically supported techniques in your practice* (pp. 272–282). New York: Wiley.

Lilliecreutz, C., Josefsson, A., & Sydsjö, G. (2010). An open trial with cognitive behavioral therapy for blood and injection phobia in pregnant women: A group intervention program. *Archives of Women's Mental Health, 13*, 259–265. doi: 10.1007/s00737-009-0126-x

Linehan, M. M. (1993a). *Cognitive-behavioral treatment of borderline personality disorder.* New York: Guilford.

Linehan, M. M. (1993b). *Skills training manual for treatment of borderline personality disorder.* New York: Guilford.

Linehan, M. M. (1995). *Understanding borderline personality disorder: The dialectic approach program treatment manual.* New York: Guilford.

Linehan, M. M. (1999). Development, evaluation and dissemination of effective psychosocial treatments: Stages of disorder, levels of care and stages of treatment research. In M. G. Glantz & C. R. Hartel (Eds.), *Drug abuse: Origins and interventions* (pp. 367–394). Washington, DC: American Psychological Association.

Marks, I. (1975). Behavioral treatments of phobic and obsessive compulsive disorders: A critical appraisal. In M. Hersen, R. M. Eisler, & P. M. Miller (Eds.), *Progress in behavior modification* (Vol. 1, pp. 65–158). New York: Academic Press.

Marra, T. (2004). *Depressed and anxious: The dialectical behavior therapy workbook for overcoming depression & anxiety.* Oakland, CA: New Harbinger.

May, G. (1982). *Will and spirit.* San Francisco: Harper & Row.

McKay, M., Fanning, P., & Ona, P. Z. (2011). *Mind and emotions: A universal treatment for emotional disorders.* Oakland, CA: New Harbinger.

McKay, M., Wood, J. C., & Brantley, J. (2007). *The dialectical behavior therapy skills workbook: Practical DBT exercises for learning mindfulness, interpersonal effectiveness, emotion regulation & distress tolerance.* Oakland, CA: New Harbinger.

Meyer, V. (1966). Modification of expectations in cases with obsessional rituals. *Behaviour Research and Therapy, 4*, 273–280.

Miller, C. (2002). Flooding. In M. Hersen & W. Sledge (Eds.), *Encyclopedia of psychotherapy* (Vol. 1, pp. 809–813). New York: Elsevier Science.

Miller, H. R., & Nawas, M. M. (1970). Control of aversive stimulus termination in systematic desensitization. *Behaviour Research and Therapy, 8*, 57–61.

Mineka, S. (1979). The role of fear in theories of avoidance learning, flooding, and extinction. *Psychological Bulletin, 86*, 985–1010.

Moonshine, C. (2008). *Acquiring competency and achieving proficiency with dialectical behavior therapy: Volume 1, the clinician's guidebook.* Eau Claire, WI: PESI.

Mowrer, O. H. (1953). Neurosis, psychotherapy, and two-factor learning theory. In O. H. Mowrer (Ed.), *Psychotherapy theory and research* (pp. 140–149). New York: Ronald Press.

Mowrer, O. H. (1960). *Learning theory and behavior.* New York: Wiley.

National Institute of Mental Health. (2009). *Anxiety disorders.* Washington, DC: Author.

Nawas, M. M., Welsch, W. V., & Fishman, S. T. (1970). The comparative effectiveness of pairing aversive imagery with relaxation, neutral tasks and muscular tension in reducing snake phobia. *Behaviour Research and Therapy, 8,* 63–68.

Neuner, F., Kurreck, S., Ruf, M., Odenwald, M., Elbert, T., & Schauer, M. (2010). Can asylum-seekers with posttraumatic stress disorder be successfully treated? A randomized controlled pilot study. *Cognitive Behaviour Therapy, 39,* 81–91. doi: 10.1080/16506070903121042

Neuner, F., Onyut, P. L., Ertel, V., Odenwald, M., Schauer, E., & Elbert, T. (2008). Treatment of posttraumatic stress disorder by trained lay counselors in an African refugee settlement: A randomized controlled trial. *Journal of Consulting and Clinical Psychology, 76,* 686–694. doi: 10.1037/0022-006X.76.4.686

Neuner, F., Schauer, M., Klaschik, C., Karunakara, U., & Elbert, T. (2004). A comparison of narrative exposure therapy, supportive counseling, and psychoeducation for treating posttraumatic stress disorder in an African refugee settlement. *Journal of Consulting and Clinical Psychology, 72,* 579–587. doi: 10.1037.0022-006X.72.4.579

New Harbinger Publications (Producer). (2011). *Introducing ACT: Learning & applying the core principles & techniques of acceptance & commitment therapy* [DVD set]. Available from www.newharbinger.com

Norberg, M. M., Krystal, J. H., & Tolin, D. F. (2008). A meta-analysis of D-cycloserine and the facilitation of fear extinction and exposure therapy. *Biological Psychiatry 63,* 1118–1126. doi: 10.1016/j.biopsych.2008.01.012

Orsillo, S. M., Roemer, L., & Holowka, D. W. (2005). Acceptance-based behavioral therapies for anxiety: Using acceptance and mindfulness to enhance traditional cognitive-behavioral approaches. In S. M. Orsillo & L. Roemer (Eds.), *Acceptance and mindfulness-based approaches to anxiety: Conceptualization and treatment* (pp. 3–35). New York: Springer.

Öst, L.-G. (1989). One-session treatment for specific phobias. *Behaviour Research and Therapy, 27,* 123–130.

Pavlov, I. P. (1927). In G. V. Anrep (Trans.), *Conditioned reflexes.* London: Oxford University Press.

Pennebaker, J. W. (1997). Writing about emotional experiences as a therapeutic process. *Psychological Science, 8,* 162–166.

Pfeifer, M., Goldsmith, H. H., Davidson, R. J., & Rickman, M. (2002). Continuity and change in inhibited and uninhibited children. *Child Development, 73,* 1474–1485.

Powers, M. B., & Emmelkamp, P. M. G. (2008). Virtual reality exposure therapy for anxiety disorders: A meta-analysis. *Journal of Anxiety Disorders, 22,* 561–569. doi: 10.1016./j.jandis.2007.04.006

Powers, M. B., Smits, J. A. J., Leyro, T. M., & Otto, M. W. (2007). Translational research perspectives on maximizing the effectiveness of exposure therapy. In D. C. S. Richard & D. L. Lauterbach (Eds.), *Handbook of exposure therapies* (pp. 109–126). Boston: Academic Press.

Prochaska, J. O., & Norcross, J. C. (1999). *Systems of psychotherapy: A transtheoretical analysis* (4th ed.). Pacific Grove, CA: Brooks/Cole.

Quilty, L. C., Van Ameringen, M., Mancini, C., Oakman, J., & Farvolden, P. (2003). Quality of life and the anxiety disorders. *Journal of Anxiety Disorders, 17,* 405–426.

Rachman, S. (1980). Emotional processing. *Behaviour Research and Therapy, 18*, 51–60.

Radomsky, A. S., Bohne, A., & O'Connor, K. P. (2007). Treating comorbid presentations: Obsessive-compulsive disorder and disorders of impulse control. In M. M. Antony, C. Purdon, & L. J. Summerfeldt (Eds.), *Psychological treatment of obsessive-compulsive disorder: Fundamentals and beyond* (pp. 295–309). Washington, DC: American Psychological Association.

Rapaport, M. H., Clary, C., Fayyad, R., & Endicott, J. (2005). Quality-of-life impairment in depressive and anxiety disorders. *American Journal of Psychiatry, 162*, 1171–1178.

Reading, A. (2004). *Hope and despair: How perceptions of the future shape human behavior.* Baltimore, MD: The Johns Hopkins University Press.

Reynolds, S. K., & Linehan, M. M. (2002). Dialectical behavior therapy. In M. Hersen & W. Sledge (Eds.), *Encyclopedia of psychotherapy: Volume 1: A–H* (pp. 621–628). San Diego, CA: Academic Press.

Richard, D. C. S., & Gloster, A. T. (2007). Exposure therapy has a public relations problem: A dearth of litigation amid a wealth of concern. In D. C. S. Richard & D. L. Lauterbach (Eds.), *Handbook of exposure therapies* (pp. 409–425). Boston: Academic Press.

Richard, D. C. S., Lauterbach, D., & Gloster, A. T. (2007). Description, mechanisms of action, and assessment. In D. C. S. Richard & D. L. Lauterbach (Eds.), *Handbook of exposure therapies* (pp. 1–28). Boston: Academic Press.

Riggs, D. S., & Foa, E. B. (2008). Treating contamination concerns and compulsive washing. In M. M. Antony, C. Purdon, & L. J. Summerfeldt (Eds.), *Psychological treatment of obsessive-compulsive disorder: Fundamentals and beyond* (pp. 149–168). Washington, DC: American Psychological Association.

Roemer, L., Orsillo, S. M., & Salters-Pedneault, K. (2008). Efficacy of an acceptance-based behavior therapy for generalized anxiety disorder: Evaluation in a randomized controlled trial. *Journal of Consulting and Clinical Psychology, 76*, 1083–1089. doi: 10.1037/a0012720

Rogers, C. R. (1957). The necessary and sufficient conditions of therapeutic personality change. *Journal of Consulting Psychology, 21*, 95–103.

Rogers, C. R. (1961). *On becoming a person.* Boston: Houghton Mifflin.

Rosqvist, J. (2005). *Exposure treatments for anxiety disorders: A practitioner's guide to concepts, methods, and evidence-based practice.* New York: Routledge.

Rothbaum, B. O., Foa, E. B., & Hembree, E. A. (2007). *Reclaiming your life from a traumatic experience: A prolonged exposure treatment program workbook.* New York: Oxford University Press.

Rothbaum, B. O., Hodges, L., Smith, S., Lee, J. H., & Price, L. (2000). A controlled study of virtual reality exposure therapy for the fear of flying. *Journal of Consulting and Clinical Psychology, 68*, 1020–1026.

Rowa, K., Antony, M. M., & Swinson, R. P. (2007). Exposure and response prevention. In M. M. Antony, C. Purdon, & L. J. Summerfeldt (Eds.), *Psychological treatment of obsessive-compulsive disorder: Fundamentals and beyond* (pp. 79–109). Washington, DC: American Psychological Association.

Roy-Byrne, P. P., & Cowley, D. S. (2002). Pharmacological treatments for panic disorder, generalized anxiety disorder, specific phobia, and social anxiety disorder. In P. E. Nathan & J. M. Gorman (Eds.), *A guide to treatments that work* (2nd ed., pp. 301–335). New York: Oxford University Press.

Ruf, M., Schauer, M., Neuner, F., Catani, C., Schauer, E., & Elbert, T. (2010). Narrative exposure therapy for 7- to 16-year-olds: A randomized controlled trial with traumatized refugee children. *Journal of Traumatic Stress, 23*, 437–445. doi: 10.1002.jts.20548

Salsman, N. (2008). Dialectical behavior therapy. In F. T. L. Leong, H. E. A. Tinsley, & S. H. Lease (Eds.), *Encyclopedia of counseling: Volume 2: Personal and emotional counseling* (pp. 571–572). Los Angeles: Sage.

Sapolsky, R. M. (1998). *Why zebras don't get ulcers: An updated guide to stress, stress related diseases, and coping* (2nd ed.). New York: W. H. Freeman.

Schauer, M., Neuner, F., & Elbert, T. (2005). *Narrative exposure therapy: A short-term intervention for traumatic stress disorders after war, terror, or torture.* Cambridge, MA: Hogrefe and Huber.

Segal, Z. V., Williams, J. M. G., & Teasdale, J. D. (2002). *Mindfulness-based cognitive therapy for depression: A new approach in preventing relapse.* New York: Guilford.

Shapiro, F. (1995). *Eye movement desensitization and reprocessing (EMDR): Basic principles, protocols, and procedures.* New York: Guilford.

Sherman, A. R. (1972). Real-life exposure as a primary therapeutic factor in the desensitization treatment of fear. *Journal of Abnormal Psychology, 79,* 19–28.

Simpson, H. B., & Liebowitz, M. R. (2006). Best practice in treating obsessive-compulsive disorder: What the evidence says. In B. O. Rothbaum (Ed.), *Pathological anxiety: Emotional processing in etiology and treatment* (pp. 132–146). New York: Guilford.

Sisemore, T. A. (2010). *Free from OCD: A workbook to help teens with obsessions and compulsions.* Oakland, CA: New Harbinger.

Smith, A. (2010, March). *A stomach of steel: Engineering exposures to treat emetophobia.* Presentation at the meeting of the Anxiety Disorders Association of America, Baltimore, MD.

Stampfl, T. G., & Levis, D. J. (1967). The essentials of implosive therapy: A learning theory based on psychodynamic behavioral therapy. *Journal of Abnormal Psychology, 72,* 496–503.

Stein, M. B., Sherbourne, C. D., Craske, M. G., Means-Christensen, A., Bystritsky, A., Katon, W. … Roy-Byrne, P. P. (2004). Quality of care of primary care patients with anxiety disorders. *American Journal of Psychiatry, 161,* 2230–2237.

Summerfeldt, L. J. (2008). Treating incompleteness, ordering, and arranging concerns. In M. M. Antony, C. Purdon, & L. J. Summerfeldt (Eds.), *Psychological treatment of obsessive-compulsive disorder: Fundamentals and beyond* (pp. 187–207). Washington, DC: American Psychological Association.

Swales, M. A., & Heard, H. L. (2009). *Dialectical behaviour therapy: Distinctive features.* New York: Routledge.

Swinson, R. P., Fergus, K. D., Cox, B. J., & Wickwire, K. (1995). Efficacy of telephone-administered behavioral therapy for panic disorder with agoraphobia. *Behavior Research and Therapy, 33,* 465–469.

Taylor, S. (Ed.). (1999). *Anxiety sensitivity: Theory, research, and treatment of the fear of anxiety.* Mahwah, NJ: Erlbaum.

Thich Nhat Hanh. (1999). *The miracle of mindfulness.* Boston: Beacon Press.

Thyer, B. A. (1981). Prolonged in vivo exposure therapy with a 70-year-old woman. *Journal of Behavior Therapy and Experimental Psychiatry, 12,* 69–71.

Thyer, B. A. (1985). Audio-taped exposure therapy in a case of obsessional neurosis. *Journal of Behavior Therapy and Experimental Psychiatry, 16,* 271–273.

Todd, J. T., & Pietrowski, J. L. (2007). Animal models. In D. C. S. Richard & D. L. Lauterbach (Eds.), *Handbook of exposure therapies* (pp. 29–51). Boston: Academic Press.

Tolin, D. F., & Steketee, G. (2007). General issues in psychological treatment for obsessive-compulsive disorder. In M. M. Antony, C. Purdon, & L. J. Summerfeldt (Eds.), *Psychological treatment of obsessive-compulsive disorder: Fundamentals and beyond* (pp. 31–59). Washington, DC: American Psychological Association.

Törneke, N. (2010). *Learning RFT: An introduction to relational frame theory and its clinical applications.* Oakland, CA: New Harbinger.

Tryon, W. W. (2005). Possible mechanisms for why desensitization and exposure therapy work. *Clinical Psychology Review, 25*, 67–94. doi: 10.1016/j.cpr.2004.08.005

Van Minnen, A., Hendriks, L., & Olff, M. (2010). When do trauma experts choose exposure therapy for PTSD patients? A controlled study of therapist and patient factors. *Behaviour Research and Practice, 48*, 1–9. doi: 10.1016/j.brat.2009.12.003

Van Noppen, B. L., Steketee, G., McCorkle, B. H., & Pato, M. (1997). Group and multifamily behavioral treatment for obsessive compulsive disorder: A pilot study. *Journal of Anxiety Disorders, 11*, 431–446.

Wald, J., & Taylor, S. (2003). Preliminary research on the efficacy of virtual reality exposure therapy to treat driving phobia. *CyberPsychology and Behavior,* 6, 459–465. doi: 10.1089/109493103769710488

Walker, C. E., Hedberg, A. G., Clement, P. W., & Wright, L. (1981). *Clinical procedures for behavior therapy.* Upper Saddle River, NJ: Prentice Hall.

Watson, J. B., & Rayner, R. (1920). Conditioned emotional reactions. *Journal of Experimental Psychology, 3*, 1–14.

Weiderhold, B. K., Gevirtz, R. N., & Spira, J. L. (2001). Virtual reality exposure therapy vs. imagery desensitization therapy in the treatment of flying phobia. In G. Riva & C. Galimberti (Eds.), *Towards cyberpsychology: Mind, cognitions and society in the Internet age* (pp. 253–272). Amsterdam: IOS Press.

Wells, A., Clark, C. M., Salkovskis, P., Ludgate, J., Hackmann, A., & Gelder, M. (1995). Social phobia: The role of in-session safety behaviors in maintaining anxiety and negative beliefs. *Behavior Therapy, 26*, 153–161.

Wolitzky-Taylor, K. B., Horowitz, J. D., Powers, M. B., & Telch, M. J. (2008). Psychological approaches in the treatment of specific phobia: A meta-analysis. *Clinical Psychology Review, 28*, 1021–1037.

Wolpe, J. (1958). *Psychotherapy of reciprocal inhibition.* Stanford, CA: Stanford University Press.

Wolpe, J. (1961). The systematic desensitization treatment of neurosis. *Journal of Mental and Nervous Disease, 112*, 189–203.

Wolpe, J. (1990). *The practice of behavior therapy* (4th ed.). New York: Pergamon.

Wood, J. J., & McLeod, B. D. (2008). *Child anxiety disorders: A family-based treatment manual for practitioners.* New York: W. W. Norton.

Yehuda, R., Marshall, R., Penkower, A., & Wong, C. M. (2002). Pharmacological treatments for posttraumatic stress disorder. In P. E. Nathan & J. M. Gorman (Eds.), *A guide to treatments that work* (2nd ed., pp. 411–445). New York: Oxford University Press.

Yoder, M., Tuerk, P. W., Price, M., Grubaugh, A. L., Strachan, M., Myrick, H., & Acierno, R. (2011, November 14). Prolonged exposure therapy for combat-related posttraumatic stress disorder: Comparing outcomes for veterans of different wars. *Psychological Services.* Advance online publication. doi: 10.1037/a0026279

Zimmerman, M., & Chelminski, I. (2003). Generalized anxiety disorder in patients with major depression: Is DSM-IV's hierarchy correct? *American Journal of Psychiatry, 160*, 504–512.

Zoellner, L. A., Abramowitz, J. S., Moore, S. A., & Slagle, D. M. (2008). Flooding. In W. T. O'Donohue & J. E. Fisher (Eds.), *Cognitive behavior therapy: Applying empirically supported techniques in your practice* (pp. 202–210). New York: Wiley.

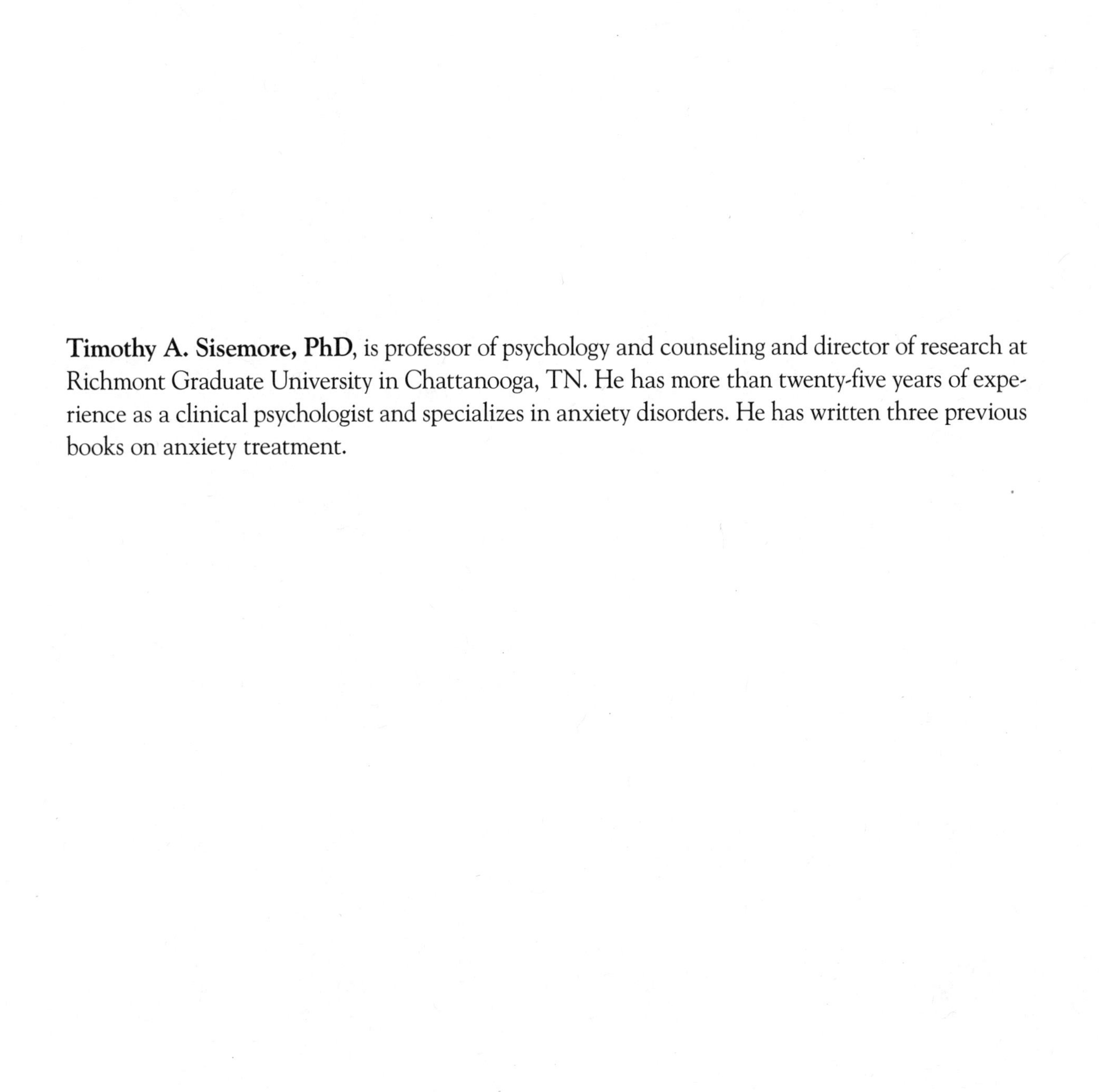

Timothy A. Sisemore, PhD, is professor of psychology and counseling and director of research at Richmont Graduate University in Chattanooga, TN. He has more than twenty-five years of experience as a clinical psychologist and specializes in anxiety disorders. He has written three previous books on anxiety treatment.

Index

A

B

C

D

E

F

G

H

I

J

K

L

M

N

O

P

R

S

T

U

V

W

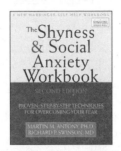